# Candida
# Can Be Fun!

Rebecca Richardson

Published by Rebecca Richardson 2011

Designed by Tin Stanton 2011
Photography by Rebecca Richardson

www.candidacanbefun.co.uk

ISBN No: 978 0 948808 14 2

Printed by Doveton Press Limited

The author stresses that the information contained in this book is to be general in nature and is not meant to be used to personally diagnose a disease or health problem.  Medical or nutritional advice should always be sought before embarking on a specific diet plan.  The contents of this book have been approved by a Qualified Nutritionist and it is strongly recommended that you seek professional advice before taking any supplements or adopting any treatments.  No responsibility can be accepted for personal actions taken without expert guidance from a trained and certified practitioner.  If you do this, you do so at your own risk.

# ACKNOWLEDGEMENTS
# (… AND APOLOGIES!)

This feels a bit like winning an Oscar!  Top of my list would have to be Katherine Dempsey, my Nutritionist, who not only got to the root of my problems (which no-one else did) but also helped me through my journey, providing me with invaluable support and encouragement to write this.  She kindly gave up hours of her time to proof read my cookbook, offer further advice and correct me when I was wrong.  She has also contributed to this book by writing a whole chapter about which supplements complement the diet.  Katherine, I owe it all to you.  You're a star.

I would also like to mention my friend, Leah, who first introduced me to Katherine.  I am extremely grateful for your cranky guts, even if you're not!

Huge thanks to Tin Stanton, who is not only a bloody good mate (and pirate), but who is also the creative inspiration and designer of this book.  You showed me that writing and publishing your own book could be done and encouraged me to fulfil my dream and made it a reality by knowing exactly which buttons to press on the computer and all that technical malarkey!  Sorry for eating all your bread on Sunday mornings back in the 1990s (oh, when I think of all that toast and what it's done to me …) and for making you listen to my singing over and over and over.  I could have done this book without you, but I didn't want to.  You're amazing!  Also thank you to Arwen for letting me borrow your husband for such a huge amount of time - you can have him back now!

Big hugs go out to my lovely Pa, who has encouraged me all the way and kept asking me over the past six years: "How's your book coming along?" just to wind me up and give me the kick in the butt to think: "I am going to write this book.  I'll show him!"  I couldn't have done it without all the 'loans' from the Bank of Father!  I'd just like to say that now I have finally completed my project, I am keen to see what he is going to patent.  Thank you for everything, Pa.  I love you.

Thanks to the rest of my wonderful family for the support offered: to Tony and Anna for being wonderful grandparents and Lotte and Chris for just being fabulous full stop; to Sam (my soulmate) for creating my web site, for loving me and treating me like a princess on a daily basis even though I am a nightmare to live with and also for having to do without all the naughty food when he hasn't even got Candida; to my lovely daughter, Edie Boo, who I never have time to play with because I'm either at work or writing a book … I'll be able to play games with you now!

Big love to Hels for being there at a moment's notice to help out and for having the time and energy to run up and down the hallway at my daughter's command for hours on end, because I haven't the time to do it myself.  You'll always be a sister to me.

I wish my mother, Vicky, was alive today to see what I have achieved.  Mum, I miss you so very much.  You should be here to share this with me.  I would like to say to my stepdad, Dave: "Thank you for being there through everything … but do avoid the recipes with the lentils in!"

Apologies to all my poor housemates and friends, especially Tim (my bro), Sazz and Jools (the Pernod posse), Julia, Barry, Marcus, Dermott and all the other people that have had the misfortune to be my housemate over the years (too many of you to name!) … I am amazed you are still speaking to me. I apologise for the emotional rollercoaster that is me, my demanding cleaning regimes and just general bouts of insanity. I am only glad that the weekend binge drinking and 3am pasta feasts haven't had a negative effect on all of your digestive systems too … yet!

Thank you to Clare and Sonny, who are always there for me when I need anything. Aside from everything else that they have given me over the years, they put me up after my return from Australia when I was possibly in my worst health and mental state. Your friendship and generosity knows no bounds.

Apologies to Claire ('Jugs') that our trip around New Zealand and Australia ended up being a chemist, clinic and toilet crawl, as opposed to the pub crawl it would normally have been! Cheers mate and I'll be round for that peppermint tea now.

To my darling, Anna, who has been through things in her life that no person of her worth and integrity should ever have had to endure. What can I say? You are an inspiration and a dear, dear friend, who makes me laugh like no other. With so very much love to you and your gorgeous family: Simon, Rosalie, Bryony, Rowan and my fairy goddaughter, Thyme.

To Vikki and Marcus for being my guinea pigs in the first round of recipes and for still being alive, slimmer and healthier to tell the tale! You've been good friends … now buy my book!

One last personal message to my friends at WTH plc, sorry for boring you senseless with tales of the progress of my book over the past year, but can you please stop filling up our office table with chocolate and cake every time I turn my back!!!! I am so grateful to Sue for proof reading this book before it went to print.

I would also like to apologise to anyone who has had the misfortune of standing next to me in the supermarket when I'm looking at product ingredients and slamming jars and cans back onto the shelves shouting: "Suuuuuuuggggggaaarrr!!".

Thank you to all the companies who have kindly allowed me to mention their brand products referred to in my recipes. Your enthusiasm, interest and offers of assistance along the way have spurred me on. I don't know what I would be eating if the brains behind the products hadn't come up with something for us "Yeasties", food intolerants and those on a restricted diet to eat without worrying about the ingredients. Thank you from the bottom of our stomachs!

A big 'thumbs up' to all you fellow Candida sufferers for posting your personal stories, experiences and recipes on the internet. It is a minefield of information and helpful suggestions. I hope this book goes some way to helping you too.

Finally, I would like to give heartfelt thanks to Erica White, the pioneer of Candida cookery. Without her relentless research and dedication to the cause, there would be literally thousands of people out there a great deal worse off. After having read Erica White's "Beat Candida Cookbook", it inspired me to write my own. She proved that it could be done, even whilst suffering with this debilitating illness. I salute you!

# CONTENTS

# CHAPTER 1

## "I'VE GOT CANDIDA!  WHAT DO I DO NOW?!"

Congratulations!  You have finally found out what is wrong with you ... you are not 'losing your marbles' after all!  Yes, Candida is pretty depressing news, but on a positive note you now have a name for your strange ailments and a 'light at the end of the tunnel'.  You CAN feel well again.  Now I want you to read the following chapters before embarking on the recipes, so you have a full overview of what it is like to be newly diagnosed with Candida and what you can and cannot have.  This is what is needed for the Survival Kit:

- A food allergy test with a qualified Nutritionist
- A clean and organised kitchen
- A well-stocked spice rack (with jars within date of expiry!)
- A steamer
- Different sized stainless steel or glass cooking pans
- A wok
- A liquidiser, hand-held blender or food processor
- Interesting crockery
- A sense of humour
- Patience of a Saint
- Compost heap/food recycling bin
- Very caring and supportive friends and family
- A bank loan!
- Diet calendar to record food and symptoms
- Herb garden
- Large freezer compartment
- Local organic butcher, farm shop or fish farm
- Access to the internet and online shopping

Before I begin, I just want to get a few things straight: I am not a professional chef, photographer or writer.  I am a normal woman (some would contend this particular point!) who works five days a week in a demanding job, is 'Mama' to a four year old (even more demanding) and is partner to long suffering Sam ... oh and let's not forget the house, its contents and the cat which also need cleaning and looking after.  Add to this already mental lifestyle an infuriating illness that can make me feel bloody awful on a daily basis, which also means that when I get home from a hard day at the office, I cannot simply pull out a plastic container from the freezer containing a meal ready to be slammed in the microwave and eaten straight from the tub ten minutes later (thus also doing away with the added inconvenience of washing up).  Sound familiar?

First things first, I am not going to tell you what Candida is; there are plenty of other books already on the market which will explain this in great detail.  My book is to be used in conjunction with these, but solely as a cookbook of recipes showing colour photographs of tasty and healthy meals that are within the parameters of this limited diet.  I like to think of it as a crash course in cooking for "Yeasties" (as we are called).  It is intended to save you all the initial leg work and make life a little easier for you at the start of your journey into the unknown.  After all, you will have plenty of time to do all the research yourself once you have a full, satisfied stomach and you know where your next meal is coming from.  I think it is also handy to have relevant information and tips from another sufferer's perspective.

The ingredients used in this book are free from the usual suspects: wheat, dairy, sugar, alcohol, fruit and other 'evils', but I have also taken the giant step of eliminating gluten products. I always recommend organic produce, if you can afford this.  This book also provides you with information on how to find the brand products on the internet, if you are not lucky enough to have local stores that stock the ones that I have used.  Once you know what is safe to eat and what is not, you will be well on your way to understanding what you are allowed and can experiment with your own dishes. Being a "Yeasty", with all the ensuing symptoms that come with it, is hard enough to cope with without having to go on a quest for the "Holy Grail" (or in this case a recipe book containing meal ideas that are decent and tasty to eat and don't contain one of the many forbidden ingredients).

When I started on this diet, I cleaned out all my kitchen cupboards (even going over them with a damp cloth – very cathartic!) and removed all the things I shouldn't be eating and either passed them on to friends or just got rid. I then stocked the cupboards with everything I could eat, so that there was nothing lurking in there that could be a temptation. This is highly recommended. If you live with your family or in a shared house, keep a separate cupboard for your own food, so you don't have to look at their 'illegal' wares.

What will soon happen is that everyone in your family and circle of friends will take a keen interest in what is wrong with you, which is great. On the downside, they will also make it their life's sole pursuit to find that one product that you have never heard of that will change your culinary life forever.

Unfortunately, this will probably result in you ending up with a kitchen cupboard full of food you can lust after, but which are unfortunately prohibited. Your 'nearest and dearest' may think that just because it says 'organic' or 'gluten-free' on the packet that you will be able to tuck in.

They don't know to look for the added 'nasties' such as dextrose, fructose, glucose, sucrose, artificial sweeteners, aspartame, saccharin, citric acid, lactic acid, vinegar, soy sauce, apple or any other fruit juice, lactose, monosodium glutamate (MSG), sodium nitrate and nitrates (meat preservatives), caffeine, alcohol ... the list goes on. Bless them for trying, but the best thing you can do is buy them a copy of this cookbook for their own use, if they suggest inviting you round for a meal. It would make a perfect present ... after all, what the hell are they going to cook you for Christmas dinner?! I can't tell you the number of times, under similar circumstances, that I have ended up having to miserably choke down some white rice, or a dish containing wheat or dairy, whilst coming across as being appreciative. In the end, I used to make all my friends come to mine for dinner, so at least I knew that what I had cooked was safe. Funnily enough, everyone used to comment on how much they enjoyed my food and how they didn't feel bloated afterwards ... "It is okay for one night, but try sticking with it for six months" I would say jokingly. However, their mood soon changed when I told them there wasn't any pudding!

So let's be out and out honest here, the majority of Candida sufferers find it extremely hard to keep to this strict diet for any longer than a month before some social event crops up, or it just all becomes too much when your work colleague starts waving a chocolate biscuit or slice of birthday cake under your nose, assuring you that "one little bit isn't going to do much harm". Make no mistake, the Candida diet is hard core, but once you start there is no turning back. You need to go all out to starve the yeast infection of what it wants. Every time you cheat, you are keeping it alive that little bit longer. The forbidden food becomes like an addiction. You crave it, you get a taste for it and your body cries out for more. Before you know it you are back to square one. This book is  going to help you get through that first month. From thereon in, it is going to be down to you and your willpower as to whether you can carry it on for another month and so on. The long and short of it is your Candida is not going to disappear by itself. If you are feeling horrible now, imagine yourself in five years' time. You are the only one who can change how you are feeling and every time you 'fall off the wagon' the only person who will suffer is you! Just remember that.

The ingredients mentioned in this book are, overall, suitable for Candida sufferers. However, there are still the awkward "Yeasties" with very specific food allergies. If my recipes contain an item you cannot eat, just replace it with something different that you can have. I've eliminated a huge amount from my recipes, but I cannot cater exclusively for every single individual with food intolerances. Therefore, I strongly suggest that you undergo a food allergy test with a qualified Nutritionist before commencing this diet. Using a number of techniques (e.g. kinesiology, VEGA allergy testing, or hair analysis testing) they will be able to identify the foodstuffs to avoid and give you advice on suitable herbal supplements to fight the Candida and boost your health. My Nutritionist (and life saver), Katherine, has kindly written a piece on supplements and holistic therapy treatments later on in Chapter 7.

Alternative therapies that have helped me on my way are acupuncture, hypnotherapy, reflexology, aromatherapy massage, yoga and reiki. I have to say that I am a fan of colonic irrigation, but I am aware that the 'jury is out' on this subject when it comes to Candida. All I can say is that I had the best and most comfortable wee that I have had in years after my very first session. You have to try all these avenues and see how they work for you. For some of you, a hose up your bottom might not appeal! All these treatments are all rather expensive though, but what else have you got to spend your money on now? You can't go out on the town on a Saturday night and spend £50 on booze and a kebab like you used to. That's a massage right there!

Instead of feeling negative about your new lifestyle, embrace it and enjoy all the good things that can come out of it, like a day at a health spa or a pampering session at the hairdressers. Work out all your frustration at the gym! You'll be feeling so good soon that you're going to want to get yourself all dolled up and buy yourself a new wardrobe of clothes because the others will be falling off you!

Candida is a very personal illness and, just to confuse matters even more, what works for you may not work for someone else. It is all a process of elimination, but very rewarding when you find out the main cause of your symptoms. The thing about combating the 'beast' is that everywhere you look on the internet people contradict what you can and cannot eat!

What I have tried to do with this book is to share what has worked for me and eliminate as many of the 'avoid' foods as much as possible, whilst leaving you with healthy, nutritious and delicious meals. I believe that potatoes, carrots, parsnips (the sweet and starchy root vegetables) can be eaten in moderation, but you will probably want to lay off the potatoes and limit the high carbohydrate foods for the first couple of weeks of your diet. Bulk up with lots of protein and greens. If you're gorging yourself on potatoes day in day out, then yes it is going to hold you back, but once in a while in small amounts this is acceptable. If you want to be even stricter on yourself then, for example, if one of my soup recipes calls for one potato, leave it out if you want to.

Try to limit fried food as much as you can, but don't set yourself up for failure by eliminating the way you cook most of your food, whilst at the same time removing half of the ingredients that you would have eaten previously! Do also pay close attention to whether my recipes state 1 'teaspoon' or 1 'tablespoon', or it could all go terribly wrong.

Tomatoes contain acid and foods high in carbohydrates like rice, potatoes, etc. are a feast for Candida. However, "I'm gonna starve this 'beast', but I ain't gonna starve myself!" As I said above, you just need to eat these items in moderation. There has to be a happy medium or "life ain't worth living".

Obviously, if you notice you do feel worse after eating a meal with, say, butter beans in, then you'll have to leave them out. You've just got to experiment. Keep off them for a week or so, then introduce them again and make a note of what happens. This is why it is good to keep a food diary. "It is a process of elimination, my dear Watson!" You can go back over it and think: "The last time I had mashed potato my silly side pain started up" or "After those tomatoes, my wee started playing up again".

On this subject, arthritis sufferers should be cautious when eating any member of the "Nightshade" family of vegetables – i.e. potatoes, tomatoes, peppers and aubergines. I thought this worth mentioning as, although there is no actual medical proof, it is believed that eating these can cause a flare up of symptoms, due to the presence of a toxin in the vegetables known as Solanine which can cause inflammation and irritation. The recipes in this book are ones that I have either thought up myself, or adapted from others which I used to cook pre-Candida (but obviously I now use alternative ingredients). I know everyone's tastes differ, but you will be surprised at what you will think is tasty once you've been on this diet for a while, as you will be so hungry.

I'm one of those cooks that throws in a little bit of this and a splash of that to see what happens. I know some of you won't be able to work like this, so I have done the best I can with measurements. Therefore, in some recipes, you may personally think an extra teaspoon of cumin is needed, or more garlic, or even less of something else, such as only half a stock cube. It is merely a guide for you to get started. You will find that you will be able to make things up as you go along once you've got into the swing of the diet. I would say that if there are ingredients in this diet you are just not sure of, then only use them rarely and see how you get on. However, remember that they are much better alternatives than what they are substituting for. You will also see I have not broken the recipes down into 'breakfast', 'lunch' and 'dinner'. This is mainly because, when on this diet, breakfast kind of goes 'out of the window'. I eat whatever I want, when I want it. Curry for breakfast? Get it down you!

A handy tip is to make as much food in one go as you can, so you can freeze it (I knew all those empty Chinese cartons would come in handy one day. Mind you, if I hadn't scoffed so much MSG over the years, I might not be in this state!). However, you need to freeze the food as soon as it has cooled to prevent mould forming on it. You will find that your appetite is insatiable and sometimes it is handy that you've made enough to feed an Army. At the start of this diet, I ended up eating two man-sized portions a night, as it is difficult to feel completely satisfied once you've eaten. You'll get days when you get very depressed at eating the same vegetables dressed up in a different way, especially when you are feeling tired and really don't have the energy to cook. That's when one of your own ready-made freezer tubs comes in handy. I have tried to vary the flavours and vegetables in each of the meals so it seems like you're having a diverse array of food. All I can say is "persevere" as it is well worth the success at the end. All those irritating aches and pains will soon disappear and all just because you are looking after yourself and building up your strength. There is a strong connection between what you eat and the health of your immune system.

For those who have struggled with a weight problem for years, you will find that the pounds drop off you like never before on any fad diet. I personally put this down to the lack of bread and sugar. You can eat ridiculous amounts of this food and still lose the pounds. However, I ought to mention that some Candida sufferers are often accused of being bulimic (myself included). Friends and family see you eating all that amount of food, but losing weight at the same time and they can't believe there is no other reason for it. Candida is a very emotional illness and your moods will be all over the place, so the last thing you will need is to have to try to convince the people who care for you that you are not sticking your fingers down your throat when their backs are turned. Nobody can understand how much this illness messes you up physically and mentally unless they have been through it themselves. I won't tell you it's not going to be difficult for the first few months, because you will probably feel worse than you did before you started.

I literally 'fell off the planet' for about four months so that I could deal with it all and not have to face the temptations out there. I wouldn't have been very good company anyway. What you have to remember is, although your symptoms are going to be exacerbated to begin with, you are actually killing the 'beast' within. I would stress that readers diagnosed with Candida (be it adult or child) who suffer with Anorexia or Bulimia will need the support of a qualified Nutritionist throughout, so they can design a programme specially tailored for your needs. Do not try to do this diet alone.

When you begin the Candida diet, you will start to experience unpleasant side effects for the first week or so, such as headaches, nausea and fatigue. This is known as the "Herxheimer Reaction". This is as a consequence of the release of toxins from the Candida fungus 'die-off'. As I said earlier, it will be nothing compared to how you will be feeling a couple of years down the line if you don't tackle it now. Embrace the pain and know it is for a good cause … and please don't blame my cooking!! There is nothing in my recipes that will make you ill, unless you are eating a specific food that you shouldn't be. Once you start taking the supplements after a month on the diet, you will start to feel a reaction. Monitor this carefully with your Nutritionist as they may want you to alter your supplement dosage to a level where you can cope with the 'die-off'. This will be explained in Chapter 7.

What you have to remember on this diet is that every little bit helps. It is very difficult for people first diagnosed with Candida to take on board the whole lifestyle change involved. Even if you can't commit to behaving yourself 100% initially, gradually change your diet so that you always have brown rice instead of white, soya margarine instead of butter, etc. Some of the recipes in this book will still include some ingredients that certain individuals cannot have, I'm sure, but that is down to their own personal food intolerances as well. This book is just a guide and I want to share it with fellow sufferers out there, as these recipes have kept me well fed! When I wasn't quite ready to commit 100% to the diet, I would decide that, firstly, the alcohol and cigarettes would go. Secondly, I would cut out the wheat and yeast, then gradually the sugar and finally the dairy. It's not the best way to do it, but it's a coping strategy which starts to get you in the mind set.

The one thing I missed most when I was first diagnosed with Candida was a glossy, photo packed, delicious looking recipe book. There are plenty of books and information on the internet explaining what Candida is, with lots of recipes available, but not one actual physical colour cookbook that eliminates everything (e.g. gluten, dairy and fruit). My dream for the future is that Nutritionists in the UK use my cookbook, so that when they diagnose their clients with Candida they can simply deliver the prognosis on a positive note, hand them a copy of my book and say: "This is what you CAN have." I hope it can help change your life for the better.

Whatever you do, when you finally reach the stage when you feel a happier and pain-free human being than you ever thought possible again, don't mess it all up and throw yourself face first into a Black Forest gateau! Your body is your temple and all that. Chances are that if you revert to your original eating habits, you are gradually going to start experiencing your symptoms again. Eat the bad food in moderation. Let your hair down occasionally, but don't binge. It is also important to say that if you do have a hiccup whilst on the diet and you go off the rails for a family wedding weekend, don't feel guilty about it, just enjoy it then get back on track as soon as you possibly can.

*Stay healthy and contented!*

# CHAPTER 2

## STAPLE INGREDIENTS - "WHAT CAN I EAT?"

Candida
Can Be Fun!

This is where I tell you what you can eat and what you can't. Hopefully you won't burst into tears like I did! You will find there is repetition of vegetables in a lot of my meals. However, we are all guilty of going to the supermarket and buying the same food every week, never wandering from the path. These are just some things that you need to be aware of on this diet:

## Complex Carbohydrates and Grains:

These are foods in wholegrain form (e.g. brown rice, wheat-free pasta, beans, millet, polenta, quinoa, maize, buckwheat, potatoes, other root vegetables, legumes, etc). They are broken down into glucose more slowly than simple carbohydrates (i.e. all the stuff we "Yeasties" aren't allowed, such as cakes, sugar, fruit, etc. which are of very little nutritional value and which our bodies just turn into fat). Complex carbohydrates therefore give us a slow, but steady stream of energy throughout the day because of the way the body processes them and the fact that they take longer to digest. Even though all carbohydrates and starches are broken down into glucose to produce energy (and us "Yeasties" are obviously trying to avoid adding more sugar to our diet) our bodies do need a certain amount of the right carbohydrates to function properly. Remember that natural complex carbohydrates are also often additive-free and preservative-free. Try to keep your carbohydrate portions to a minimum by eating them with other vegetables and not at every meal. Bulk up with protein and vegetables. The usual advice is to keep your intake of carbohydrates low for the first couple of months on the Candida diet and this includes all root vegetables (such as carrots, swede, turnip, potato, sweet potato) – e.g. one small serving of potato or other root vegetable daily and don't overload your plate with lots of brown rice or wheat-free pasta.

Life without bread ... just deal with it! I am not going to raise your hopes by offering you any gluten-free alternatives made with soya flour or the like ... it will only look (and taste) like a brick. I can guarantee it won't be that delicious, warm from the oven, mouth-watering, doorstop slice you think it is going to be. Your spirit will only be dashed and you'll end up kneading over a hot stove only to throw it in the bin disheartened and bloody hungry. Put all thoughts of bread to the back of your mind ... that is until you are cured and you can have a total toast-fest!

## Dairy:

Cow's milk is to be avoided at all cost. Some Candida diets say it is okay to supplement this with goats' milk, yoghurt and feta cheese. However, you are rarely able to obtain organic substitutes and even feta cheese contains lactose, which is not allowed. For the most part, it seems people struggling with Candida are able to include some non-aged, non-moldy cheeses or plain yoghurt in their diets with little to no reaction. These cheeses include (but are not limited to) mozzarella, goat, rice, feta, and cream cheese. It may be okay from time to time, but you would need to see how you tolerate it and then only have it very rarely as a treat. As I am not 100% convinced, I have not included any cheese recipes in this book. As a replacement for milk, I use a specific brand of soya milk and instead of adding cream to my cooking I use coconut milk, but only the tinned brands that produce it with just coconut and no other additives. However, you cannot beat making your own from a real coconut (if you have the time).

## Drinks:

What you can drink is obviously limited. I really miss my cups of tea and glasses of red wine! However, what I don't miss is what they did to my bladder! The more water you imbibe the better to flush out the toxins. Drink as much as your bladder can manage! The daily recommended amount is eight glasses a day. However, everyone is different and if your bladder is as over-active as mine, then you won't be able to manage this amount and hold down a steady job! My Office Manager would have to move my computer into the toilet!

Alternatives to your normal cup of tea or coffee (which don't taste absolutely revolting) would be: still or fizzy mineral water (add a slice of lemon to liven it up), herbal teas (e.g. camomile, peppermint and rooibos). There are some great Ayurvedic herbal teas available too, but check the ingredients carefully. I make a lovely hot drink using sliced up fresh lemon and fresh ginger. Homemade carrot and lemon juice made in a liquidizer is delicious, but don't overdo it.

The type of sugar that carrots contain raises blood sugar very rapidly, but as the amount of sugar is low they are still allowed on the diet because of their high fibre content and the fact that they also contain beta-carotene, which is extremely important as a pro-vitamin and also an antioxidant.

Also, hot soya milk with a grating of nutmeg or cinnamon on top is nice as a bedtime tipple. Make sure you check the soya milk ingredients very carefully. I have only come across one brand (mentioned in Chapter 3) that just contains soya beans and nothing else. Many manufacturers love to slip in some derivative of sugar or fruit juice.

One thing I should talk about here is "detoxing" your body; this is where you drink only certain liquids for a whole day and do not eat solid foods. This would not be a good idea, as it will put more stress on your liver and that is working overtime as it is. If you are following the diet and using the recommended supplements, you are doing enough.

Fat:

Hydrogenated fats are a 'no no'! These are the fats that are solid or semi-solid at room temperature. They may taste great, but they raise cholesterol and play havoc long-term with your heart. You will see from the recipes that rapeseed oil (aka canola), extra virgin olive oil, sunflower oil and avocado oil are my main cooking oils of choice. You can use any of these and substitute one for another in my recipes. Extra virgin olive oil is healthy and provides a mix of mono-unsaturated and poly-unsaturated fats (the good ones). However, these can also be found in oily fish, avocados and seeds. It has a fairly high cooking temperature, but I would recommend rapeseed oil or sunflower oil for frying, as they have a higher smoke point. There are a number of other oils which are recommended, such as safflower oil and linseed oil, but these are harder to come by. Safflower oil and avocado oil have a high content of Vitamin E, which is good for your health. Remember that the less processed the oil, the healthier it is for you. Also the less frying and roasting you can do the better, but I know that this isn't always possible. Try to grill or bake your food. There are a number of fried/roasted recipes in this book which I consider as a treat. Let's face it, we don't get many! For the purposes of the Candida diet, I also use non-hydrogenated dairy and gluten-free spreads (also mentioned in Chapter 3). As long as you are using fats and oils sparingly in your cooking and preparation, it would be fine to use any of the "good" oils above. Alternatively, if you want to cut down on your oil intake, you can substitute the oil for a little water, or stock to soften onions, etc.

Fruit and Vegetables:

"5 a day … more like 15!" A major downfall with Candida is that you are not allowed fruit, because of the high fructose levels. The only fruits allowed are tomato, avocado, lemon and olives (provided the jar variety do not contain vinegar, lactose or citric acid). I buy either the fresh green queen olives stuffed with garlic or pimento from a deli, or for black olives my favoured type is Crespo (available from Tesco).

Here is a list of just some of the vegetables you are able to eat.  This list is by no means exhaustive:

| | | | | |
|---|---|---|---|---|
| Artichoke | Aubergine | Asparagus | Bean sprouts | Beetroot |
| Broad beans | Broccoli | Brussel sprouts | Butternut squash | Cabbage (all) |
| Calabrese | Carrot | Cauliflower | Celeriac | Celery |
| Chard | Chinese leaf | Courgette | Cucumber | Fennel |
| Jerusalem artichoke | Kale | Kohl rabi | Leek | Lettuce (all) |
| Mange tout | Mung beans | Onion | Pak choi | Parsnip |
| Petit pois/peas | Peppers (all) | Potato | Pumpkin | Radish |
| Runner/green beans | Shallots | Spinach | Spring onions | Sugar snap peas |
| Swede | Sweet corn | Sweet potato | Swiss chard | Turnip |
| Tomato (all) | Watercress | | | |

Vegetables provide a good mix of vitamins, minerals, calcium and iron (amongst other things) and keep the immune system healthy.  They are low in fat and high in fibre.  Vegetables are much better for you raw or steamed, so they still have a bite to them and retain the essential vitamins.  Always use organic vegetables when you can. I know organic produce can be pricey and not often easy to come by in the local supermarket, but they do have a lesser amount of chemicals in and, let's face it, they taste how a vegetable should taste.  There are a number of companies around now (i.e. Riverford, Abel & Cole, Laverstoke Park Farm, Sheepdrove Farm, etc.) who deliver organic produce to your door weekly (including organic meat and eggs) which makes life easier.  There is sometimes mud to wash off though!  However, in the current climate, food

is very expensive and if you have a family or four or more to feed, you most certainly cannot afford to do this at every meal.  In this case, I would suggest treating yourself to an organic bag of the vegetables you most eat (e.g. carrots) and buy other organic produce as and when you can afford it.  It's the same with meat and that is why at least half of these recipes are vegetarian, as it's the cheaper option.  One thing that you have to remember is that some vegetables do have a high sugar content naturally occurring (e.g. high glycemic index vegetables).  You must learn to be sensible and eat these certain vegetables in moderation (e.g. root vegetables, beans, artichokes, corn, etc.).  High fibre, low starch vegetables such as broccoli, celery, radish, asparagus, green leafy vegetables and alfafa help to cleanse the colon and intestinal tract and also promote acidophilus growth and discourage yeast reproduction.  Vegetables such as broccoli, asparagus and lettuce should be a daily part of your diet.  Vegetables that inhibit the growth of Candida are: onions, garlic, root ginger, cabbage, broccoli, turnips and kale.  Raw onions and garlic are very good natural antifungals.

For the Candida sufferers who have bladder problems (e.g. Interstitial Cystitis), you might want to consider going one step further and look into a low oxalate/bladder friendly diet.  It may be that you could be sensitive to a certain group of foods.  Try doing some investigating by keeping a food diary and find out what your trigger foods might possibly be. Luckily for us Interstitial Cystitis sufferers, the majority of the ingredients used in this book should not cause your symptoms to flare up, but just keep a record of what you have eaten on the day things do and take it from there.

## Gluten:

Some Candida recipe books include glutenous foods, but I want to keep this recipe book as simple as I can, so have omitted these. There is nothing worse than starting this diet only to find that two weeks down the line you've been eating something you shouldn't. I made this mistake at the beginning by cooking lots of snacks made from oats. It was such a blow when I realised that oats contain gluten and it made me very depressed, leaving me feeling like I had to start all over again … with even less to eat than I had thought previously. Gluten is a starch and therefore a basic sugar, so you may find that you will binge on products containing gluten for this very reason, so it is good to avoid it.

## Herbs and Spices:

I always tend to use fresh herbs in the recipes, as they do not harbour mold like many dried varieties, plus they have a far more potent flavour to them and add more colour to the dishes. They just simply taste nicer. Examples of fresh herbs that I use are: garlic, root ginger, coriander, basil, dill, parsley, chives, mint, lemon thyme, tarragon, rosemary and sage. It is also worth mentioning that most fresh herbs can be frozen. I have often bought a packet of parsley for some extortionate price only to find that two days later it has gone off. To save money, freeze the rest of the pack once you've used it and then you have the herbs to hand in the freezer when you need them. If you have a herb garden even better, as you can pick on demand. The best herbs to freeze are mint, parsley, coriander, basil, chives and tarragon. They keep their flavour better having been frozen, rather than dried. I have heard that it is best to blanch the herbs first by dipping them quickly into boiling water, then iced water and pat them dry before freezing. Put them into handy little tubs and label them. (I often save my old shop bought hummus tubs for just this purpose, as the herbs do crumble, so this protects them from being squashed by the occasional lump of organic lamb on the freezer shelf). You can also freeze herbs in ice cube trays. Chop the herbs coarsely and add one tablespoon of water to each tablespoon of herbs.

Spices kept in sealed jars have a long shelf life. However, I would suggest making sure they don't date back to the late 90's, like I discovered most of mine did! I advocate using cayenne pepper as a replacement for chilli (however, if you suffer adverse reactions to this, please leave it out of your cooking). It is the same pepper that gives chilli its kick, but it is gentler on the digestive system. As it is an aid to increasing circulation, the goal of cayenne pepper on the Candida diet is to improve circulation, cleanse the body and promote healing. Out of all the spices, I would say that chilli would be the main one to avoid. However, I do use the following spices: Chinese five spice, cinnamon sticks, cumin seeds, fenugreek, ground cinnamon, ground coriander, ground cumin, ground ginger, mustard seeds, nutmeg and paprika (the mild variety!). There are a range of spices produced by Bart Spices and Suma, which are excellent quality.

In the recipes, you will see that I have added 'sea salt and freshly ground black pepper to taste'. You will need to reduce your salt intake. However, I know from personal experience it is difficult to eliminate it immediately, especially when we are cutting out so many other ingredients that you would normally eat. I am a salt fiend, but as well as increasing the sugar levels in your blood, too much salt can lead to a higher risk of stroke and heart disease ... as if you didn't have enough to worry about! Therefore, it is best to use either Lo Salt (mostly potassium) or sea salt. A craving for salt can indicate a zinc deficiency. Freshly grind your own black peppercorns when needed to reduce the mold content which can be present in peppermills.

I need to mention garlic, as the size of garlic bulbs do vary (see image). I use the very large ones (one clove being the size of three cloves of one you would buy from a bulb in the supermarket). For the purposes of this cookbook, therefore, I will leave it to you to decide how much garlic to add to your food, based on what you are already used to. I don't want to be accused of making you a social outcast!

## Protein:

To ensure you help build and repair cells and muscles, your diet must contain protein foods. For the purposes of the Candida diet, what you are allowed is lean meat, such as poultry and fish. Red meat can be eaten on special occasions, but it does tend to have inflammatory properties and this does not bode well for our various ailments, so is best avoided on a regular basis. Lamb is a favourite of mine, or sometimes when I'm feeling lethargic, I will treat myself to a sirloin beef steak to boost my iron levels. I always buy organic meat to avoid the synthetic hormones, antibiotics or chemicals, which are a killer to Candida sufferers. It is more expensive, but definitely worth it. I would rather go without meat than eat a cheap, antibiotic filled chicken. Ugh! Also aim to eat omega 3-rich oily fish at least once a week (e.g. salmon or trout - watch out for bones). However, do not eat prawns too often as apparently they can congest the liver and that particular organ is going to be doing overtime as it is! Tinned tuna is handy (either in spring water, brine or sunflower oil) but try not to eat more than one tin a week because of the mercury levels in this. Eggs are allowed in this book, as long as they are organic, free-range ones, but try not to eat more than five eggs in one week.

## Pulses and Legumes:

For convenience, a few of the tinned vegetables/pulses available on the market are suitable for use, as long as you check they do not contain sugar, or any other disallowed ingredient (e.g. vinegar, citric acid or lactic acid). These include black eyed beans, butter beans, gungo (pigeon peas), chick peas, fava beans, pinto beans, red kidney beans, red lentils, green lentils and chana dhal. I buy mine in the local Asian supermarket (www.sweetmart.co.uk) as most of the brands are free from all the 'nasties' and are also reasonably priced. Suma and Biona both do a great range of these also, including citric acid-free tinned tomatoes. You can also buy these online, as well as in some supermarkets. Most other tinned products contain salt, so make sure you rinse them really well before using. When I mention tinned produce in my recipes, please note that the weight stated is the weight of the tin and not the drained weight. However, if you want to be on the safe side and avoid additional salt content, then you need to buy the freeze dried pulses/beans and cook them yourself. However, this usually means planning a day ahead to soak and boil them before you can use them. I would recommend using 100g dried beans for every 400g of tinned cooked beans, as they expand as they rehydrate, and do some research into preparing the different sorts of beans, as cooking times may vary for each type.

## Seeds and Nuts:

These can be used as a snack to nibble on, or scattered over a salad or pasta dish. The seeds allowed are: pumpkin, sunflower, flax (linseed), poppy seeds and sesame seeds. I avoid all nuts, whether they have just been cracked or not, with the exception of pine nuts.

## Sugar and Sweeteners:

Forget it! Nothing is allowed in this book. In fact, the most controversial ingredient is probably a bit of carob in the ready-made gravy powder I recommend and I even contemplated leaving that out. Some diets advocate the use of stevia, but I go on the premise that if it tastes sweet, it probably isn't doing you any good, no matter if it is natural! I am afraid that you are just going to have to put all thoughts of pudding or cakes out of your mind. You'll be surprised, but your sweet tooth will gradually disappear. When I would want something that was slightly sweet flavoured, I would eat some fresh coconut (not the desiccated stuff). Hardly a substitute for a sticky bun, but it's something nonetheless.

You have to remember that sugar is evil, it tastes bloomin' marvellous, but it is a short-lived synthetic high which leaves you flat afterwards and wanting more.

# CHAPTER 3

## BRAND PRODUCTS USED IN THIS BOOK

Candida
Can Be Fun!

The following staple ingredients referred to in this chapter are also suitable for vegetarians and vegans, but I would always recommend that you check the labels first to be on the safe side. This list is by no means exhaustive. It is simply a taster of what is out there. I would like to thank these companies for taking the time and trouble to create these brands for us. The products listed below are free from wheat, gluten, sugar (and various derivatives of), yeast, vinegar, citric acid, dairy products (cows' milk and lactose ingredients) and are not genetically modified. None of these products are fermented, or contain alcohol, preservatives, artificial additives, chemicals, colouring agents or hydrogenated oils. Unfortunately, I cannot confirm that these products will not have, at some point, come into contact with nuts or other serious allergens throughout their processing, but none actually contain nuts. Those of you with a nut or other severe allergy need to be as vigilant as ever.

However, I do need to point out that some of the other products that the brand companies below offer in their range will **not** be appropriate. Therefore, I have merely referred to the specific products that are safe for us "Yeasties" and food intolerants to use. **Always** check the label.

As us "Yeasties" are so limited in what we can actually eat, we have to make do with what restricted, alternative products are available to us on the market and thank goodness there are more and more appearing. Unfortunately, you have to cover some miles to try and find them and do some real research, which is why the internet is so wonderful. My hope is that I can limit the hard work you have to do at the beginning of your quest. I would mention that it is worth visiting the web sites listed in the next chapter, as some other allowed products are available for purchase on these sites. There is also a wealth of additional information to be had. If the products do not list the actual ingredients, just drop the company an email and ask someone to check these for you before you commit to buy. They are really helpful.

### Allergycare Gluten-Free Gravy Powder   www.gfdiet.com

This comes in a 300g tub. Ingredients: Potato starch, hydrolysed vegetable protein, carob powder, salt, onion powder, spice extracts and herb extracts. I have allowed this on this diet, even though it has a little potato starch and carob powder in it. I doubt you will be using it on a daily basis, so therefore I believe the intake would be negligible for you. It is worth it just to have a Sunday roast, or a Shepherd's Pie now and then. It really is delicious. Allergycare also sell gluten-free flour (e.g. millet and buckwheat) and some egg replacement items for vegans.

This Allergycare product is available from a few web sites: www.goodnessdirect.co.uk, www.ethicalsuperstore.com, www.healthstore.uk.com and www.wheatanddairyfree.com.

### Biona Organic Tomatoes, Tinned Pulses & Beans, Organic Corn Spaghetti Nests   www.windmillorganics.com

The tomatoes are citric acid-free and only contain tomatoes and tomato juice. They come in 400g tins of either whole cherry tomatoes, chopped peeled tomatoes or whole plum peeled tomatoes. There are other makes out there too, but you just need to find the ones that contain just tomatoes and nothing else. These are really tasty and good quality.

Biona's selection of pulses and beans are not only really handy, but organic too and stored only in water with no salt or sugar. The range is from chick peas through to aduki beans, haricot beans, butter beans, green lentils, red kidney beans, black beans, to mention a few. A quick and easy option for when you've forgotten to soak your chick peas the night before! It took me almost two days to make my last batch of hummus from scratch! Thank you for making life easier, Biona.

… and just when you thought it couldn't get any better, Biona also produce organic corn spaghetti nests. These are really quick and easy to make and taste just as good as wheat spaghetti, if not better.

The Biona range is widely available from a variety of good health food shops and organic supermarkets and online at: www.planetorganic.com, and www.goodnessdirect.co.uk, as well as many others. They can also be purchased in some of the Waitrose, Ocado and Morrisons stores.

**Bragg Liquid Aminos**  *www.bragg.com*
This is a great substitute for soy sauce for use in stir-fry meals. It comes in a 32 fl oz (1 quart) sized bottle and also a handy sized 6 fl oz/180ml spray bottle. Ingredients: Bragg's formulated soy protein is from Certified Non-GMO Healthy Soybeans and purified water only. This product has a small amount of naturally occurring sodium. Bragg Liquid Aminos has just received NON-GMO certification by the NON-GMO Project in the United States, the highest standard for NON-GMO products. Bragg Liquid Aminos can be purchased from: www.yourhealthfoodstore.co.uk, www.bevital.co.uk and www.planetorganic.com, to name but a few online stores.

**Clean Bean Tofu**  *www.ssba.info/Tenants/cleanbean.html*
This finest quality organic tofu is fresh and unpasteurised.
Ingredients: Water, organically grown soya beans and nigari.

Due to the short shelf life of this product, the company only currently distribute in the London area. However, it is available from Planet Organic and also online as part of an add-on to an organic vegetable box from: www.organicdeliverycompany.co.uk. Other than that, Clean Bean Tofu is available in London health food shops, like Wholefoods and small independents like Mother Earth, Earth Natural Foods, The Haelan centre, The Grocery, etc.

**Clear Spot Tofu**  *www.clearspottofu.co.uk*
Unlike the vast majority of prepared products, R&R Tofu use no emulsifiers, stabilisers or gums of any kind and use 'nigari' to coagulate the soya 'milk', so that their curd holds together extremely well. This tofu can also be frozen.
Ingredients: Water, organic soya beans and nigari.

Clear Spot tofu is available online from: www.goodnessdirect.co.uk, www.abelandcole.co.uk, www.naturalgrocery.co.uk and www.holosfoods.com.

**Clearspring Avocado Oil, Dried Sea Vegetables and Sea Salt**  *www.clearspring.co.uk*
The avocado oil comes in a 250ml bottle. Ingredients: Organically grown avocados. This can be used for deep-frying, sautéing, baking, casseroles and dressings. It is low in saturated fats, high in mono-unsaturated fats and cholesterol-free. It also contains vitamin E. They also do a selection of organic cold pressed oils. The web site is well worth a visit just for its informative section on 'Choosing a quality oil' and 'Oil nutrition and cooking temperatures'.

The dried sea vegetables come in 25g and 50g bags and are quite expensive (around £4.50 a pack), but you use them so rarely you can treat yourself. There are a number of types of seaweed available in this range (e.g. kombu, wakame and nori).

The traditional sea salt is available in a 250g bottle.

Clearspring's products are available through independent health food shops across the UK and Ireland - visit the Clearspring web site to find stockists. However, they can also be purchased online at: www.healthysupplies.co.uk, www.planetorganic.com and www.goodnessdirect.co.uk.

**Dairy-Free Parmazano and Cheddareese**  *www.mh-foods.co.uk*
The Parmazano comes in a 60g shaker and is a great replacement for grated mature hard cheese, such as parmesan.
Ingredients: Soya flour (75%), non-hydrogenated vegetable oils (15%), rock salt, flavouring, antioxidant: vitamin E.

The Cheddareese also comes in a 60g shaker. Ingredients: Soya flour (75%), non-hydrogenated vegetable oils (17%), rock salt, flavouring, antioxidant: vitamin E. It makes such a difference to have something to sprinkle over your bolognese.

These two products can be found online at: www.mh-foods.co.uk, www.planetorganic.com, www.ocado.com and www.wheatanddairyfree.com, to name but a few.

**Free & Easy Gluten-Free Vegetable Gravy Sauce Mix**  *www.healthysales.co.uk*
This comes in a 130g tub. Ingredients: Brown rice flour, cornstarch* (non-GM), hydrolysed vegetable protein (non-GM) extract of roasted barley malt* (gluten-free), powdered onion, sea salt and ground pepper. *NB – Again, I doubt you will be using this gravy on a daily basis, so I believe the cornstarch and roasted barley intake would be negligible for you to have occasionally.

This Free & Easy product is available from the following sites: www.naturallygoodfood.co.uk, www.goodnessdirect.co.uk, www.ethicalsuperstore.com, www.wheatanddairyfree.com and www.myagelesslifestyle.co.uk.

**Hummus**
You cannot beat making your own, but if you do not have the time, then most of the major supermarkets sell them in handy-sized tubs.

Sainsbury's actually sell an organic one, which is the one that I favour. As always, check the ingredients so that no sugar or citric acid is in there.

**Kallo Organic Corn Cakes, Rice Cakes and Yeast-Free Stock Cubes**  *www.kallofoods.com*
The Kallo corn cakes come in a 130g pack.
Ingredients: Wholegrain maize (organically grown) and salt.

The Kallo rice cakes come in 100g and 130g packs. Ingredients: Wholegrain brown rice and salt. Other types of rice cake are also available in this range (e.g. sesame rice cakes, low fat rice cakes and unsalted rice cakes).

The stock cubes come in a pack of six. Ingredients: Sea salt, hydrolysed soya and maize protein, vegetable fat, carrot (3.5%), onion (3.5%), tomato (2%), herbs (lovage, parsley), spices (celery seed, pepper, mace, turmeric). I would be lost without these, I honestly would. If you don't have the time to constantly make vegetable stock, these are an absolute life-saver.

You can buy this range in most major supermarkets and health food shops, but also online at the following sites: www.goodnessdirect.co.uk, www.naturallygoodfood.co.uk, www.holosfoods.com and www.ethicalsuperstore.com, to mention but a few.

**King Soba Noodles**  *www.kingsoba.com*
These are organic and come in 250g packs consisting of three separate wraps of noodles. They come in a variety of flavours – e.g. Millet and Brown Rice, Buckwheat, Corn and Brown Rice, Black Rice Noodles and Brown Rice, Pumpkin, Ginger and Brown Rice and Wakame, and the new organic and fair trade Pad Thai Vermicelli noodles. They are quick, easy and are a great staple ingredient.

These noodles can be purchased from a number of organic supermarkets, but also online from the following: www.ethicalsuperstore.com, www.wheatanddairyfree.com, www.naturalgrocery.co.uk and www.greenbeanorganics.co.uk.

**Lemon Juice**
Nothing beats the real thing. I always use organic, unwaxed lemons. However, most bottled varieties are also acceptable and handy, but do check the ingredients before using.

**Marigold Braised Tofu**   *www.marigoldhealthfoods.com*
The braised tofu comes in a 225g tin. Ingredients: Dried soya bean curd (85%), water, safflower oil, liquid aminos made from soya and maize, millet extract and sea salt.

This product can be purchased from Holland & Barrett stores and also online at: www.goodnessdirect.co.uk and www.holosfoods.com.

**Merchant Gourmet Sun-Dried Tomatoes and Slow Roasted Tomatoes**   *www.merchant-gourmet.com*
The Merchant Gourmet sun-dried tomatoes come in a 100g packet. They are quick and easy to use. You just need to soak them in warm water for 30 minutes. Ingredients: Sun dried tomatoes.

The Merchant Gourmet slow roasted tomatoes come in a 100g packet. No need to soak, you can eat them straightaway. Ingredients: Tomatoes.

These products can be purchased direct from the Merchant Gourmet web site and from some of the major supermarkets or online at: www.ocado.com.

**Mrs Crimble's Corn Cakes**   *www.mrscrimbles.com*
These come in a 140g box of 4 stay fresh packs containing 5 cakes. Ingredients: Corn (99.7%) and sea salt. They are a handy snack or lunch with a topping.

These can be bought in some major supermarkets, or online from: www.goodnessdirect.co.uk, www.simply-free.co.uk and www.gffdirect.co.uk, as well as many other web sites.

**Orgran Pasta**   *www.orgran.co.uk*
The corn pasta comes in a 250g bag. Ingredients: Maize meal 100%.

The rice & millet pasta comes in a 250g bag. Ingredients: Stoneground brown rice (93%) and wholegrain millet (7%).

The vegetable rice pasta spirals come in a 250g bag. Ingredients: Brown rice 99% and vegetables (spinach and beetroot) 1%.

There are a number of other pastas in this range, varying in ingredients and shape. You will never go back to wheat pasta again. Orgran pasta doesn't leave you bloated and it tastes great. The Orgran range is available from: www.naturallygoodfood.co.uk, www.goodnessdirect.co.uk, www.healthysupplies.co.uk and www.holosfoods.com, as well as many other sites and major supermarkets.

**Provamel Organic Soya Unsweetened Milk (Red Carton)**   *www.provamel.co.uk*
The milk comes in a 1 litre or handy 500ml carton. Ingredients: Water, hulled organic soya beans (7.2%).

NB - The Provamel organic unsweetened soya milk in the red coloured carton is the only product which I have found on the market so far that does not contain any derivative of sugar or fruit juice. However, be careful you check the ingredients, as the Provamel soya milk brand in the orange coloured carton does contain maltodextrin. Always buy the red carton.

This product can be found in certain Holland & Barrett stores and small health food shops and can be bought online from the following sites: www.ethicalsuperstore.com, www.planetorganic.com and www.naturallygoodfood.co.uk.

**Pure Dairy-Free Spreads**  *www.puredairyfree.co.uk*

Pure soya dairy-free spread: This spread comes in a 500g tub.  Ingredients: Soya oil (45%), water, palm oil, salt (0.75%), emulsifier (mono and diglycerides of vegetable fatty acids), vitamin E, natural flavouring, vitamin A, colour (natural carotenes), vitamin D as D2 and vitamin B12.

Pure sunflower dairy-free spread:  This spread also comes in a 500g tub.  Ingredients: Organic oils (sunflower (35%), palm) water, salt (1.4%), emulsifier (soya lecithin), organic concentrated carrot juice, natural flavouring, vitamin A and vitamin D as D2.

Pure olive dairy-free spread:  This comes in a 500g tub and is a 59% vegetable fat spread.  Ingredients: Water, vegetable oils, olive oil (18%), extra virgin olive oil (3%), salt (0.75%), emulsifier (mono-and diglycerides of fatty acids), vitamin E, natural flavouring, vitamin A, colour (natural carotenes), vitamin D2, vitamin B12.  Vegetable oils: Palm and sunflower.  Colour: Natural carotenes.

These spreads can now be bought in most major high street supermarkets.

**Suma Tinned and Dried Pulses and Beans, Tomato Purée, Passata and Herbs and Spices**  *www.suma.coop*

Suma provides a wide range of 100% vegetarian, organic, fair trade and ethically sourced products.  Their range of tinned beans contains no sugar or salt, or you can purchase their dried pulses and beans instead.  They make tomato puree and passata free from citric acid.  There is a vast choice of herbs, spices and oils.  They also produce a vegan spread, as well as eco-friendly household cleaning products.

Suma have a great web site, which is well worth a visit just for the wealth of interesting information, but you can also buy their products direct online from there.  Suma goods are also available from certain health food shops and: www.ethicalsuperstore.com, www.goodnessdirect.co.uk and www.naturalgrocery.co.uk.

**Sunita Organic Polenta, Tahini and Olive Oils**  *www.skoulikas.com*

The polenta comes in a 500g ready-made block.  Ingredients: Water, maize flour, salt, acidity regulator (tartaric acid).

The tahini comes in both dark and light varieties, which are available in 340g jars.  Ingredients: Sesame seeds.

The Sunita organic oil range is excellent and can be purchased online from various outlets.  Always use the best quality oil when you can afford it.  There are lots of varieties out there, but some can be costly.  Treat yourself, you're worth it!

The Sunita products are available in certain health food shops in the UK and are also available for purchase at the following websites: www.ethicalsuperstore.com and www.goodnessdirect.co.uk.

**Tomato Purée**

There are some tubes of this which are citric acid-free (e.g. Suma and Biona).  However, make sure you check the label. I have used this as a substitute for tomato ketchup when having an egg.

The recipes in this book incorporate use of the above brands, but when you get the hang of the diet you will soon discover new foods and products that you can have and start creating masterpieces of your own!  What you have to remember is that I am not a qualified Chef.  I am just someone who enjoys cooking and, unfortunately for me, eating. You are welcome to adapt the recipes in any way you like.  If you think a meal could do with something else added, go for it (e.g. add 4 cloves of garlic instead of 2).  If you personally think it's worth it, try making your own gluten and yeast-free bread.  You might be happier with a substitute instead of going completely without like I am.  Everyone's taste is different.  Feel free to experiment.  It's what I did.  I just hope my ideas give you a little more hope for the challenging months ahead of you.

*"Happy eating!"*

# CHAPTER 4

## WEB SITES

If you are not lucky enough to have any local health food shops or organic stores nearby, then you are still able to buy your food in bulk online. Here are a handful of web sites that stock some of the various healthy alternatives that us "Yeasties" need and you can also obtain further information on the products from their relevant web sites.

Please note that these web sites were all active at the time of going to print and I cannot be held responsible if the companies do not continue to operate. You can always type the name of the foods you are attempting to source into a search engine on the internet and it should hopefully come up with alternative sites where you can find them. Do remember that you will be charged postage & packaging on top of your shopping and this can be pricey when buying chilled or frozen produce. I like to make sure I buy in bulk, so as to keep costs down on P&P.

*"Happy shopping!"*

www.247healthfoods.co.uk
www.aardvark-wholefoods.co.uk
www.abelandcole.co.uk
www.bartspices.com
www.beautynaturals.co.uk
www.bevital.co.uk
www.biocare.co.uk
www.biona.co.uk
www.bragg.com
www.clearspring.co.uk
www.clearspottofu.co.uk
www.ethicalsuperstore.com
www.faceofflowers.co.uk
www.gfdiet.com
www.gffdirect.co.uk
www.glutenfree-foods.co.uk
www.goodnessdirect.co.uk
www.grecianfoodsonline.co.uk
www.greenbeanorganics.co.uk
www.healthstore.uk.com
www.healthysales.co.uk
www.healthysupplies.co.uk
www.holosfoods.com
www.kallofoods.com
www.kingsoba.com
www.laverstokepark.co.uk

www.marigoldhealthfoods.com
www.merchant-gourmet.com
www.mh-foods.co.uk
www.mrscrimbles.com
www.myagelesslifestyle.co.uk
www.natracare.com
www.natural-alternative-products.co.uk
www.naturalcollection.com
www.naturalgrocery.co.uk
www.naturallygoodfood.co.uk
www.ocado.com
www.orgran.co.uk
www.planetorganic.com
www.provamel.co.uk
www.puredairyfree.co.uk
www.riverford.co.uk
www.sheepdrove.com
www.simply-free.co.uk
www.skoulikas.com
www.spiritofnature.co.uk
www.ssba.info/Tenants/cleanbean.html
www.suma.coop
www.sweetmart.co.uk
www.wheatanddairyfree.com
www.windmillorganics.com
www.yourhealthfoodstore.co.uk

# CHAPTER 5

## RECIPES

Candida
Can Be Fun!

# RECIPES

All Day Breakfast
Asian Vegetable Salad
Aubergine Roast with Quinoa
Avocado & Tomato Salad
Baked Beans
Baked Salmon with Dill Vegetables
Baked Sweet Potato with Tuna & Baby Corn
Barbecued Wild Black Sea Bream
Bean Salad
Beef Mulligatawny Soup
Beef Tacos
Black Bean Jambalaya
Blackened Herb Salmon with Watercress & Potato Salad
Broccoli Soup
Butternut Squash Stuffed with Vegetable Rice
Cajun Pork Stew with Black Olives
Carrot & Butter Bean Soup
Chicken in Basil & Tomato
Chicken Kebabs with Roasted Vine Tomatoes
Chicken Saag
Chicken Soup
Chicken Stew
Chicken with Mediterranean Lentils
Chicken with Potato Salad and Red Cabbage & Pine Nut Salad
Chick Pea & Cherry Tomato Pasta
Chinese Chicken with Noodles
Cod & Courgette Bean Salad
Coleslaw
Courgette & Butternut Squash Pasta
Creamy Celery Soup
Crispy Herbed Potatoes
Crunchy Veggie Stir-Fry
Egg Fried Rice
Fish Pie
Friday Night Mish Mash

Fried Egg, Potato Cake & Tomato

Greedy Guts Salad

Guacamole Dip with Tortilla Chips

Hummus

Hungarian Aubergine with Polenta

Kedgeree

King Prawn Indian Lemon Rice

King Prawns in Garlic & Parsley 'Butter'

King Prawn Skewers with Noodle Salad

Lamb & Vegetables with Quinoa

Lamb Paprika Stew

Lambs' Lettuce Salad

Lamb with Lentils

Lemon Quinoa with Chicken Kebabs

Marinated Tuna with Summer Roasted Vegetables

Mayonnaise

Meatballs & Spaghetti Sauce

Millet & Tofu Scramble

Minestrone Soup

Mixed Vegetables in Gravy

Nasi Goreng

Onion Bhaji

Parsnip Soup

Passata

Pesto Cod with Lambs' Lettuce Salad

Pesto Dressing

Pork Casserole with Broccoli & Mash

Potato Salad

Prawn Curry

Quick & Easy King Prawn Spaghetti

Ratatouille

Red Cabbage & Pine Nut Salad

Rhubarb & Spinach Curry

Rice Cakes with Crab Topping

Roast Chicken with Lemon Gravy & Sesame Seed Parsnips

Roasted Red Pepper & Garlic Pesto

Roasted Romano Peppers with Quinoa Salad

Roasted Vegetable Quinoa
Sage & Onion Stuffing Balls
Salmon & Scrambled Egg
Salmon Fishcakes with Salsa Dip
Salsa Dip
Seaweed & Spicy Chick Pea Soup
Shepherd's Pie
Spaghetti Bolognese
Spicy Butternut Squash Soup
Spicy Lentil Soup
Spinach Soup
Steak with Baked Potato & Wilted Baby Spinach
Stir-Fried Tofu with Chop Suey & Rice
Stuffed Marrow
Sunday Lamb Roast
Tabbouleh
Thai Noodle Soup
Trout with Avocado & Tomato Salad
Tuna & Kidney Bean Salad
Tuscan Bean Soup
Vegetable & Olive Pasta
Vegetable Omelette
Vegetable Pilaf
Vegetarian Paella
Veggie Cayenne
Warm Chicken Salad with Red Pepper & Fennel
Watercress & Potato Salad
Watercress Soup

 Vegetarian or Vegan, depending whether it has an egg in the recipe!

# All Day Breakfast

Yes, it is a great shame that we can't add crispy bacon and a fat Cumberland sausage to the mix, but think of the long-term effects on your heart. This is a healthy and filling meal without the saturated fat!

**Serves 1**

*2 tablespoons of sunflower oil*
*1 small red onion (peeled and sliced)*
*1 fresh tomato (halved and cored)*
*10 thin slices of ready-made polenta (chopped)*
*1 large organic egg*
*Baked Beans (see recipe)*
*Sea salt and freshly ground black pepper to taste*

In a large frying pan, add 1 tablespoon of oil.
When hot, fry the onion on a medium heat for about 5 minutes, stirring regularly.
Spoon the onion to one side of the pan to keep warm.
Put the halved tomato (seed side down) in the frying pan next to the onion and leave it there to warm.
Add the polenta and maybe a little more oil, if needed.
Cook on a medium heat for 4 - 5 minutes. Stir continuously until a similar consistency to mashed potato.
If frying your egg, add 1 tablespoon of oil and fry it in the spare corner of the frying pan.
Otherwise, poach or soft boil the egg, if you would prefer.
In a small saucepan, warm up the required amount of Baked Beans (see recipe) on a medium heat.
On a dinner plate, serve up the onion, polenta, egg and beans.
Eat straightaway with a piping hot cup of peppermint tea.

# Asian Vegetable Salad

This is a unique salad to take to a party or barbecue. You can also give it a few squirts of Bragg Liquid Aminos to give it an Oriental flavour! It also goes well with Fish Pie (see recipe).

**Serves 4 - 6**

*10 baby corn (boiled or steamed)*
*¼ small sweetheart or white cabbage (shredded)*
*85g (3oz) of fresh watercress*
*¼ cucumber (sliced and quartered)*
*1 small carrot (peeled and sliced julienne)*
*2 spring onions (trimmed and sliced thinly)*
*5 radishes (trimmed and sliced)*
*½ yellow pepper (cored, deseeded and sliced)*
*2 handfuls of fresh bean sprouts*
*3 teaspoons of sesame seeds*
*2 tablespoons of freshly chopped basil*
*1 tablespoon of fresh lemon juice*
*Sea salt and freshly ground black pepper to taste*

In a small pan, on a medium heat, cook the baby corn for about 4 - 5 minutes (or you can steam them).
In a colander, place the baby corn to drain then set aside to cool.
Finely slice/shred the cabbage and roughly chop the watercress, then add to a large salad bowl.
Quarter the cucumber and cut the carrot into thin 1 inch sticks. Mix in with the cabbage and watercress.
Slice the spring onions, radishes and yellow pepper.
Add these to the bowl together with the raw bean sprouts and sesame seeds.
Chop the basil leaves roughly and sprinkle over the vegetables.
Drizzle over the lemon juice and add salt and pepper to taste.
Mix the salad together with your hands.
Cover the bowl with cling film, return to the fridge to chill and eat within 24 hours.
You can always halve the quantity of ingredients if you don't want to make as much.

# Aubergine Roast
## with Quinoa

It's always a challenge to cook for someone who is vegetarian or vegan, let alone without the use of mushrooms and cheese, so you can impress your friends with this delicious meal!

### Serves 2 - 3

1 medium aubergine (trimmed and cut into 1cm thick rings)
½ teaspoon of sea salt
2 tablespoons of rapeseed oil
1 tablespoon of fresh lemon juice
1 heaped teaspoon of chopped fresh root ginger
1½ tablespoons of Bragg Liquid Aminos
200g (7oz) of quinoa
1 pint of vegetable stock
1 red pepper (cored, deseeded and chopped)
1 medium courgette (trimmed and grated coarsely)
Sea salt and freshly ground black pepper to taste

Prepare the aubergine by trimming both ends.  Slice into 1½ cm thick rings and rub liberally with sea salt.
Leave to sit for 20 minutes.  Wash off the salt from both sides well with cold water and pat dry.
This process removes much of the bitterness and reduces fat absorption.  (You can choose not to do this).
Preheat the oven to 180°C/350°F/gas mark 4.
In a large frying pan, heat the oil.  On a medium heat, fry the aubergine until brown on both sides.
Lay the aubergine flat on a roasting tray, so that it is just one layer.
In a measuring jug, mix the lemon juice, ginger and Bragg Liquid Aminos.  Pour over the aubergine.
Roast in the oven for 10 minutes, then turn the slices over and cook for a further 10 minutes.
In a sieve, rinse the quinoa with cold water and drain.  In a wok, toast the quinoa on a low heat for a minute.
Add the stock to the quinoa and stir well.  Cover with a lid.
Simmer on a low heat for about 15 minutes, stirring often until all the water is absorbed.
(Note that the grain will turn from white to transparent and the spiral-like tail will appear when it is cooked).
In the frying pan, stir-fry the pepper and courgette on a medium heat for about 5 minutes.
Add this to the quinoa in the wok.  Mix thoroughly.  Remove the aubergine from the oven.
Layer the aubergine on a plate and spoon the quinoa on top.  Add another layer of aubergine and quinoa.

# Avocado & Tomato Salad

This is a tasty, fresh salad, which is great for a lunch, or an accompaniment to an evening meal. It goes well with Trout (see recipe). It's quick to make and fun to design!

**Serves 2**

*1 large ripe avocado (peeled, de-stoned and sliced)*
*I large fresh beef tomato (sliced and cored)*
*1 small red onion (peeled and sliced)*
*5 fresh basil leaves*
*1 teaspoon of extra virgin olive oil*
*½ tablespoon of fresh lemon juice*
*1 tablespoon of pumpkin seeds*
*Sea salt and freshly ground black pepper to taste*

Slice the avocado into two halves, then peel and de-stone it.
Cut the avocado into thin slices.
Wash and slice the beef tomato, removing the green core.
Peel and slice the onion then cut into solid rings.
Lay the avocado, tomato and onion on a serving plate in a design of your own choice.
Lay the basil leaves on top.
Drizzle the oil and lemon juice over the salad.
Sprinkle the pumpkin seeds over it.
Serve immediately.

# Baked Beans

As an alternative to dill, you can change the flavour of the beans by adding a pinch of cinnamon, mustard powder, allspice, paprika and 1 tablespoon of Bragg Liquid Aminos instead.

**Serves 2 - 3**

*2 tablespoons of extra virgin olive oil*
*1 large clove of garlic (peeled and crushed)*
*1 small red onion (peeled and finely chopped)*
*½ red pepper (cored, deseeded and finely chopped)*
*1 x 400g tin of tomatoes (or 4 fresh peeled tomatoes)*
*1 tablespoon of tomato purée*
*1 x 400g tin of cannellini beans (or 100g dried)*
*1 tablespoon of freshly chopped parsley*
*25g (3 tablespoons) of freshly chopped dill*
*Sea salt and freshly ground black pepper to taste*

If using tinned beans, drain them in a colander and rinse thoroughly with cold water and set aside.
If you are going to use dried beans, you will need less in weight as they expand in size as they rehydrate.
You will need to prepare 100g of dried beans per 400g tinned beans and soak them for the required time.
Follow the relevant instructions for cooking the particular types of beans from dried.  Tinned are so easy!
In a large frying pan, heat the oil.
Add two-thirds of the chopped garlic (save the rest for the end), together with the onion and red pepper.
Fry on a medium heat for about 5 minutes until softened, stirring regularly.
Pour in the tomatoes and stir in the tomato purée.
If you prefer and you have the time, you can use fresh tomatoes, peeled and cored, instead of tinned.
Cook on a low heat for 2 - 3 minutes.
You can blend the sauce with a hand-held blender for a couple of seconds, if you want it smooth.
However, I leave it as it is so that there is still some texture to the bean sauce.
Add the beans, parsley, dill and rest of the raw garlic.
Warm through and serve as part of the All Day Breakfast, or on top of a baked potato.
In this recipe, you can also change the beans to whatever shape and size you like (e.g. butter beans).

# Baked Salmon
## with Dill Vegetables

Here's a handy tip... when steaming your vegetables, use just enough water to cook them (without burning your pan!). That way the vegetable stock will be more concentrated.

**Serves 1**

*1 fresh salmon fillet*
*1 knob of dairy and gluten-free spread*
*½ unwaxed, organic lemon*
*2 new potatoes (washed and halved lengthways)*
*1 medium carrot (peeled and cut julienne)*
*1 small leek (trimmed and sliced)*
*1 tablespoon of freshly chopped dill*
*Sea salt and freshly ground black pepper to taste*

Preheat the oven to 180°C/350°F/gas mark 4.

Cut a piece of foil big enough to wrap the salmon fillet in a loose parcel.

Place the salmon on this and add a knob of spread on top and drizzle over 1 teaspoon of lemon juice.

Close up the foil and place it on a baking tray in the oven for about 20 minutes.

In the bottom pan of a steamer, add the potatoes and pour over enough boiling water to cover them well.

Add the carrots to a steaming tray above the potatoes 5 minutes after the potatoes start cooking.

Steam for about 10 - 15 minutes, or until the vegetables are done to your taste. Do not overcook.

In a frying pan on a low heat, add a knob of spread. Melt it, add the leek and stir until soft.

When the potatoes are done, drain them in a colander (but save the water as vegetable stock to freeze).

Place the cooked salmon on a plate with the other vegetables.

Pour the juices from the foil over the salmon/potatoes and sprinkle with the dill.

Garnish with some slices of lemon.

# Baked Sweet Potato
## with Tuna & Baby Corn

Obviously you need to limit the amount of potato you eat on this diet, but occasionally this recipe is fine. Save the rest of the tuna mixture to have on some rice cakes as a snack later on in the day.

### Serves 1

*1 small to medium sweet potato (washed and trimmed)*
*1 x 185g tin of tuna in sunflower oil, brine or spring water*
*75g (2½oz) of tinned sweet corn*
*2 tablespoons of hummus*
*¼ small red onion (peeled and chopped finely)*
*1 knob of dairy and gluten-free spread*
*1 handful of green beans (boiled or steamed)*
*4 baby corn (boiled or steamed)*
*Sea salt and freshly ground black pepper to taste*


Wash the potato, cut off the ends and prick around the potato with a knife.

Lay some foil on a baking tray and place the potato on this (to save on washing up).

Bake the potato in an oven preheated to 190°C/375°F/gas mark 5 for about 50 minutes.

Drain the liquid from the tuna and put in a bowl. (At this stage, I like to share some with my cat!)

Mix in the sweet corn, hummus and onion with the tuna. Stir well.

When the potato is tender, remove it from the oven, put on a plate, halve it and mix in some spread.

Add the required amount of the tuna mixture to the top of the potato.

Serve with green beans and baby corn, which have been boiled or steamed for about 5 minutes.

# Barbecued Wild Black Sea Bream

This is the sort of meal you won't eat every day, so treat yourself. It's also a lovely recipe to take to a barbecue. Nobody will want their burgers when they see this!

## Serves 2

*1 whole wild black sea bream (scaled and gutted)*
*2 tablespoons of extra virgin olive oil*
*2 large cloves of garlic (peeled and crushed)*
*1 small onion (peeled and chopped finely)*
*1 unwaxed, organic lemon (juice and rind)*
*1 tablespoon of freshly chopped rosemary*
*Sea salt and freshly ground black pepper to taste*

Heat the barbecue until very hot. (Note that this can as easily be cooked by oven or grill).
Wash the fish and pat it dry with kitchen towel. Make slashes around 4 cm apart on both sides.
In a large measuring jug, add the oil, garlic, onion, lemon juice, lemon rind and rosemary. Stir well.
On a large sheet of foil, spoon some of the mixture on and place the fish on top.
Fill the cavity with some of the mixture and spread the rest over the top.
Make sure the marinade soaks well into the cuts.
Wrap the fish up in the foil parcel and marinate in the fridge for about 1 hour.
Grill the fish on the barbecue for 3 - 4 minutes on each side whilst in the foil.
Then carefully remove the fish from the foil and scrape the onion mixture to one side for later.
Gently place the fish on the barbecue to cook the skin on both sides.
When slightly blackened, remove from the barbecue and serve on a bed of salad.
Pour over remaining marinade from the foil.
Serve with a green salad or potato salad.
(Note: Do be very careful of the fish bones).

# Bean Salad

This is a really simple and quick salad to make.  It is a good side dish for a nice piece of fish, or an organic chop or chicken breast.  Alternatively, you can just eat it on its own as it is.

### Serves 3 - 4

*1 red pepper (cored, deseeded and quartered)*
*1x 400g tin of black eye beans (or 100g dried)*
*1x 400g tin of cannellini beans (or 100g dried)*
*1 large handful of fresh parsley (chopped)*
*2 tablespoons of extra virgin olive oil*
*2 teaspoons of fresh lemon juice*
*Sea salt and freshly ground black pepper to taste*

If using tinned beans, drain them in a colander and rinse thoroughly with cold water and set aside.
If you are going to use dried beans, you will need less in weight as they expand in size as they rehydrate.
You will need to prepare 100g of dried beans per 400g tinned beans and soak them for the required time.
Follow the relevant instructions for cooking the particular types of beans from dried.  Tinned are so easy!
Quarter the pepper and remove the seeds.
Place the pepper pieces skin side up on foil on a grill pan and grill until blackened.
When the pepper has cooled sufficiently, remove the skin.
Chop up the pepper into small pieces and add to a large salad bowl
Add the beans to the dish with the other ingredients.
Grab a handful of fresh parsley (roughly the same size as the amount of beans).
Chop the parsley and add to the bowl with the oil and lemon juice.  Stir thoroughly
Refrigerate before serving.

# Beef Mulligatawny Soup

Cooking brown rice is an art, so if my method doesn't work out for you, refer to the pack instructions. Sam and I always disagree on how to best cook brown rice and have our own way of doing it!

**Serves 4 - 6**

*2 tablespoons of extra virgin olive oil*
*2 large cloves of garlic (peeled and chopped)*
*1 teaspoon of fenugreek*
*1 teaspoon of ground cumin*
*1 teaspoon of ground coriander*
*1 teaspoon of turmeric*
*200g (7oz) of organic beef steak (chopped in chunks)*
*2 medium carrots (peeled and diced)*
*½ small swede (peeled and diced)*
*2 stalks of celery (trimmed and sliced)*
*1 red pepper (cored, deseeded and chopped)*
*2 pints of vegetable stock*
*1 x 400g tin of tomatoes (or 4 fresh peeled tomatoes)*
*115g (4oz) of brown basmati rice*
*Fresh coriander to garnish*
*Sea salt and freshly ground black pepper to taste*

In a large cooking pan, heat the oil, garlic (two-thirds of it) and spices.
Add the beef and stir-fry for about 2 minutes on a medium heat until the meat is sealed.
Put in the vegetables and add the stock, together with the tomatoes.
Simmer on a low heat for about 1 hour, until the beef is tender. Stir regularly. Add the remaining raw garlic.
In a separate pan which has a lid, pour in about ¾ pint of boiling water and a small drop of oil.
In a sieve, add the rice and rinse well with cold water then add the rice to the pan.
Cover and simmer on a low heat, stirring occasionally, for about 25 - 30 minutes until cooked.
In a colander, drain the cooked rice then rinse well with boiling water until the water runs clear.
Blend the soup with a hand-held blender until almost smooth (leave some chunks of vegetables for texture).
Add the cooked rice after you have finished blending. You can mix it in or arrange it in the centre.
Serve immediately with a sprinkling of fresh coriander.

# Beef Tacos

For a perfect night in with friends, serve these with guacamole, hummus and salsa for a full Mexican meal. My four year old daughter also loves these (but my cat prefers tuna).

### Serves 3 - 4

*500g (17½oz) of organic beef mince*
*2 large cloves of garlic (peeled and crushed)*
*1 medium carrot (peeled and diced)*
*1 red pepper (cored, deseeded and diced)*
*1 teaspoon of freshly chopped oregano (or dried)*
*1 teaspoon of ground cumin*
*1 teaspoon of mild paprika*
*¼ teaspoon of cayenne pepper (optional)*
*1 x 400g tin of tomatoes (or 4 fresh peeled tomatoes)*
*2 tablespoons of tomato purée*
*1 packet of plain taco shells*
*3 leaves of iceberg lettuce (shredded)*
*Sea salt and freshly ground black pepper to taste*

Heat a wok on a medium heat. Add the beef mince and fry until it browns. Stir constantly to prevent it burning.
Break up the mince as it cooks and then drain off any excess oil (possibly about 6 tablespoons!!)
Add the garlic and spices to the beef mince and fry for a further couple of minutes, stirring occasionally.
Put in the carrot and pepper and stir-fry for about 5 - 10 minutes until they soften.
Mix in the tomatoes and tomato purée.
Cover and simmer for about 15 - 20 minutes, stirring often until the carrots and peppers are cooked.
Preheat the oven to 180°C/350°F/gas mark 4.
Place the taco shells on a tray with the top opening end down in the middle of the oven for 2 - 3 minutes.
Stuff the shells with the meat mixture and lettuce.
Serve with some Hummus, Guacamole and Salsa Dip (see recipes).

# Black Bean Jambalaya

This recipe can be served traditionally by adding rice, or you can eat it as a side dish with a delicious organic roast chicken. Whichever way you have it, it's sure to be a winner!

**Serves 4 - 6**
*2 tablespoons of extra virgin olive oil*
*3 teaspoons of freshly chopped oregano (or dried)*
*1 teaspoon of ground coriander*
*1 teaspoon of ground cumin*
*1 teaspoon of ground turmeric*
*3 large cloves of garlic (peeled and chopped)*
*1 large onion (peeled and diced)*
*1 red pepper (cored, deseeded and chopped)*
*1 large carrot (peeled and diced)*
*1 stick of celery (trimmed and diced)*
*1 large fresh bay leaf*
*2 x 400g tins of tomatoes*
*1 yeast-free vegetable stock cube*
*2 x 400g tins of black beans (or 200g dried)*
*Sea salt and freshly ground black pepper to taste*

If using tinned beans, drain them in a colander and rinse thoroughly with cold water and set aside.
If you are going to use dried beans, you will need less in weight as they expand in size as they rehydrate.
You will need to prepare 100g of dried beans per 400g tinned beans and soak them for the required time.
Follow the relevant instructions for cooking the particular types of beans from dried. Tinned are so easy!
In a large wok or saucepan, heat the oil. Add the spices, oregano, garlic and onion.
Fry on a medium heat for about 5 minutes and stir until softened. Put in the red pepper, carrot and celery.
Stir-fry for about 10 minutes until cooked. Add the tomatoes and bay leaf.
In a jug, make up the stock cube with 100ml/4 fl oz of boiling water and pour into the pan. Stir well.
Cover with a lid. Simmer on a low heat for about 10 minutes, or until the vegetables are cooked to your taste.
Pour in the cooked black beans and warm through, stirring regularly. Serve with brown basmati rice and salad.

# Blackened Herb Salmon
## with Watercress & Potato Salad

This is a messy job, but well worth it.  Cover the pan with the lid of a wok to prevent oil spatters all over your stove and up the wall.  This saves on cleaning!

**Serves 2**

½ teaspoon of black peppercorns (crushed)
1 tablespoon of freshly chopped rosemary
1 tablespoon of freshly chopped lemon thyme
1 tablespoon of freshly chopped parsley
1 tablespoon of freshly chopped mint
4 tablespoons of sunflower oil
¼ teaspoon of sea salt
1 - 2 teaspoons of fresh lemon juice (to taste)
2 salmon fillets (skin on, but boneless)
1lb (16oz) of small new potatoes (quartered)
75g (2½oz) of fresh watercress
14 cherry tomatoes (halved)
2 tablespoons of pumpkin seeds
2 - 3 tablespoons of homemade Mayonnaise (see recipe)

In a mortar and pestle, crush the black peppercorns.
Chop up the herbs finely.
In a flat, shallow dish, add the oil, herbs, salt and black pepper and lemon juice.
Place the salmon fillets in the oil mixture, coating all sides.
Please note that not all of this oil will actually be consumed.
If you have the time, cover the dish with cling film and leave to sit for up to 1 hour in the fridge.
In a hot griddle pan, fry the salmon on a medium to high heat.
Open a window or door to the outside, as it gets quite smoky in the kitchen.  Cover the pan with a lid.
Cook for 10 - 15 minutes in all, turning onto each side once.
If they are thick fillets, lie on all four sides and cook for longer if you like your fish well done.
The herbs and salmon skin will become nice, crispy and edible.
Serve hot with Watercress & Potato Salad (see recipe).

# Broccoli Soup

This soup makes for an easy lunch if you have a microwave at your place of work, or take it in with you in a flask like we used to do in the old days!

**Serves 4**

1 large knob of dairy and gluten-free spread
1 large clove of garlic (peeled and crushed)
1 large leek (trimmed, peeled and sliced)
1 large onion (peeled and chopped)
1 medium carrot (peeled and chopped)
2 stalks of celery (trimmed and sliced)
1 medium head of broccoli (chopped in pieces)
2 pints of vegetable stock
1 tablespoon of fresh lemon juice
2 tablespoons of tomato purée
2 fresh bay leaves
½ pint of organic, unsweetened soya milk
1 teaspoon of freshly chopped spinach to garnish
Sea salt and freshly ground black pepper to taste

In a large pan with a lid, heat the spread (or alternatively you can use 1 - 2 tablespoons of sunflower oil).
When the spread has melted, add the garlic, leek and onion.
Stir on a medium heat for about 5 minutes until they soften, then add the carrot, celery and broccoli.
Mix well then pour in the stock, lemon juice, tomato purée and bay leaves.
Simmer for 30 minutes or until the vegetables are cooked.  Remove bay leaves.
Add the soya milk, warming through gently (if overheated the soya milk goes frothy).
Wait for it to cool a little then blend with a hand-held blender.
Serve with 1 teaspoon of freshly chopped spinach or chives, or a grating of nutmeg to garnish.

# Butternut Squash
## stuffed with Vegetable Rice

This recipe serves two people, but if there is any rice left over you can put this in a tub and it can be frozen for a lunch or a spare evening meal. It's always handy to have emergency back-up!

### Serves 2

2 tablespoons of rapeseed oil
1 small butternut squash (halved and deseeded)
1 large clove of garlic (peeled and sliced)
225g (8oz) of brown basmati rice
½ teaspoon of turmeric
1 large clove of garlic (peeled and chopped)
1 small red onion (peeled and chopped)
2 medium carrots (peeled and cubed)
¼ small swede (peeled and cubed)
¾ pint of vegetable stock
85g (3oz) of red lentils
85g (3oz) of petit pois
Sea salt and freshly ground black pepper to taste

Preheat the oven to 200°C/400°F/gas mark 6.
Cut the squash in half lengthways and scoop out the seeds with a spoon and discard them.
Place the squash on a baking tray. Drizzle with oil and 1 clove of sliced garlic. Bake for about 45 minutes.
In a large pan with a lid, pour in 1½ pints of boiling water, a small drop of oil and the turmeric.
In a sieve, add the rice and rinse well with cold water then put the rice in the pan.
Cover and simmer on a low heat, stirring occasionally, for about 25 - 30 minutes until cooked.
In a colander, drain the cooked rice then rinse well with boiling water until the water runs clear. Set aside.
In a wok or large pan, heat 2 tablespoons of oil. Cook the chopped garlic and onion on a medium heat until soft.
Add the carrot, swede, stock and lentils. Mix thoroughly and simmer with a lid on for about 15 - 20 minutes.
Stir regularly until the vegetables and lentils are cooked.
Add the petit pois just before the end to prevent them from overcooking. Stir in the cooked rice.
Lay the butternut squash on the plate and fill the centre with the vegetable rice.
Serve with salad and a sprinkling of dairy-free Parmazano and seeds.

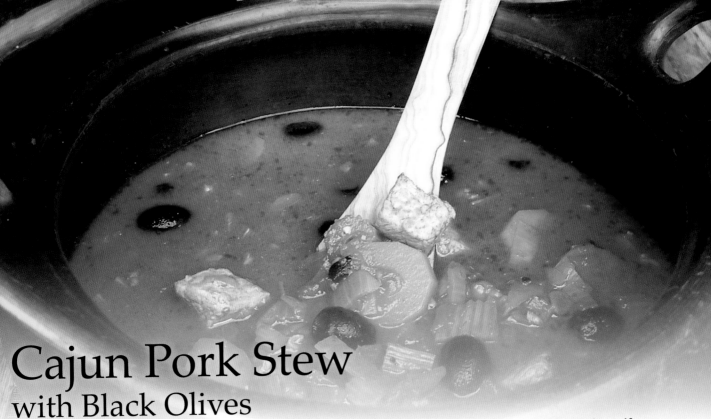

# Cajun Pork Stew
## with Black Olives

This hearty dish can also be served with noodles or polenta, if you fancy a change from rice.  If you are vegetarian or vegan, then you can substitute the meat with aubergine or squash, for example.

**Serves 4**

*1 tablespoon of extra virgin olive oil*
*1 organic pork loin chop (sliced into cubes)*
*1 tablespoon of mild paprika*
*1 teaspoon of ground coriander*
*1 teaspoon of oregano*
*¼ teaspoon of cayenne pepper (optional)*
*½ teaspoon of ground cumin*
*2 large cloves of garlic (peeled and crushed)*
*1 large onion (peeled and diced chunkily)*
*1 large carrot (peeled and sliced)*
*2 stalks of celery (trimmed and sliced chunkily)*
*1 x 400g tin of tomatoes (or 4 fresh peeled tomatoes)*
*1 pint of vegetable stock*
*3 tablespoons of tomato purée*
*Sea salt and freshly ground black pepper to taste*

In a large stainless steel pan with a lid, heat the oil.
Add the pork and stir-fry this on a medium heat for about 3 - 4 minutes.
Stir in the spices with the meat.
Add the garlic (two-thirds of it) and the onion.
Put in the carrot, celery and tomatoes.
Add the stock and tomato purée.  Mix thoroughly.
Cover with a lid and simmer on a low heat for about 30 minutes, stirring occasionally to prevent burning.
Taste some pork to see if it falls apart when you bite into it.  Cook for a little longer if not.
Add the rest of the raw garlic towards the end of the cooking time.
This meal can be served on its own, or on a bed of cooked brown rice as an evening meal.

# Carrot & Butter Bean Soup

This dish is great for a Saturday lunch, sat around the kitchen table with the family and a tower of rice cakes in the middle! What better way to spend your weekend.

**Serves 3 - 4**

*3 - 4 large carrots (peeled and grated)*
*1 - 2 tablespoons of extra virgin olive oil*
*1 large clove of garlic (peeled and crushed)*
*1 large red onion (peeled and chopped)*
*1 large leek (trimmed and sliced)*
*2 pints of vegetable stock*
*1 small potato (peeled and chopped)*
*2 fresh tomatoes (peeled, cored and chopped)*
*2 tablespoons of tomato purée*
*1 tablespoon of freshly chopped parsley*
*1x 400g tin of butter beans (or 100g dried)*
*Sea salt and freshly ground black pepper to taste*

If using tinned beans, drain them in a colander and rinse thoroughly with cold water and set aside.
If you are going to use dried beans, you will need less in weight as they expand in size as they rehydrate.
You will need to prepare 100g of dried beans per 400g tinned beans and soak them for the required time.
Follow the relevant instructions for cooking the particular types of beans from dried. Tinned are so easy!
Peel and grate the carrots and leave them to one side.
In a large cooking pan with a lid, heat the oil.
On a medium heat, fry the garlic, onion and leek for about 5 minutes until soft, stirring regularly.
Add the stock, potato, tomatoes, tomato purée and half of the grated carrot to the pan. Mix in well.
Cover the pan and simmer for 15 - 20 minutes, stirring occasionally. Remove from heat.
When cooled slightly, blend the soup mixture a little with a hand-held blender to thicken it.
Add the rest of the grated carrot and the parsley to the soup.
Simmer for a further 15 minutes so that the grated carrot still has a little bite to it.
Finally, stir in the butter beans and warm through.
Serve immediately, or freeze for future lunches.

# Chicken in Basil & Tomato

You can use one organic chicken breast in this recipe instead, if you would prefer it to thigh. Also you can serve this dish with brown rice, or eat it on its own as a stew, if you are avoiding potatoes.

### Serves 3 - 4

*1 tablespoon of rapeseed oil*
*2 organic chicken thighs (skin and bone removed and cubed)*
*1 large onion (peeled and chopped)*
*1 green pepper (cored, deseeded and chopped)*
*2 fresh tomatoes (peeled, cored and chopped)*
*1x 400g tin of tomatoes (or 4 fresh peeled tomatoes)*
*1 tablespoon of tomato purée*
*2 large cloves of garlic (peeled and crushed)*
*2 tablespoons of freshly chopped basil*
*New potatoes*
*½ savoy cabbage (sliced thinly)*
*1 small knob of dairy and gluten-free spread*
*Sea salt and freshly ground black pepper to taste*

In a wok, heat the oil.
Add the chicken, onion and pepper. Cook for a few minutes on a medium heat until the chicken is done.
Pour in the fresh and tinned tomatoes (the use of two types of tomatoes is just for the texture).
Add the tomato purée and garlic and a small amount of water, if necessary.
Cover with the lid and simmer for about 10 - 15 minutes, stirring regularly.
Boil the potatoes for about 20 minutes - do not overcook.
Steam the cabbage for about 10 - 15 minutes over the potatoes and keep the stock for freezing.
Add a knob of spread to the cabbage, if required.
Serve everything up on a plate and enjoy!

# Chicken Kebabs
## with Roasted Vine Tomatoes

These kebabs always go down a storm in my house. You can slightly change the vegetables, or even the marinade, on another occasion, just to have a bit of variation in your diet. Delicious!

### Serves 2

*1 organic chicken breast (skinless and cubed)*
*1 small courgette (sliced into chunks)*
*1 red pepper (cored, deseeded and cut in chunks)*
*1 medium red onion (peeled and quartered)*
*1 tablespoon of extra virgin olive oil*
*1 small clove of garlic (peeled and crushed)*
*1 tablespoon of fresh lemon juice*
*2 tablespoons of extra virgin olive oil*
*4 vine ripened tomatoes (still on the vine)*
*1 tablespoon of extra virgin olive oil*
*Sea salt and freshly ground black pepper to taste*

Slice the chicken into large cubes.
Cut the courgette, pepper and onion into bite-sized pieces.
Place the chicken and vegetables in a large bowl.
Pour over 1 tablespoon of oil, the garlic and lemon juice. Add a pinch of salt and pepper.
Stir thoroughly, coating the chicken and vegetables in the marinade.
Allow to sit for about an hour in the fridge.
Preheat the oven to 180°C/350°F/gas mark 4.
On a foil covered baking tray, place the vine tomatoes and drizzle with 1 - 2 tablespoons of oil.
Cook the tomatoes in the oven for about 10 minutes (or until the skin is slightly wrinkled).
Turn off the oven and place the tomatoes on the bottom shelf to keep warm.
Thread the chicken and vegetables onto some skewers and grill for about 10 - 15 minutes each side.
Turn regularly, until all the ingredients (especially the inside of the chicken) are cooked thoroughly.
Serve the kebabs on a plate with the roasted tomatoes.

# Chicken Saag

If you are a big curry fan, you will love this dish. You are not able to have garlic naan bread or chapati with this, but you can serve it with some plain poppadoms, either shop bought or made yourself!

## Serves 2

2 tablespoons of extra virgin olive oil
3 large cloves of garlic (peeled and chopped)
2 medium leeks (trimmed and sliced)
1 teaspoon of turmeric
½ teaspoon of cumin seeds
½ teaspoon of ground coriander
2 teaspoons of fenugreek
1 organic chicken breast (cubed)
300g (10½oz) fresh spinach (or spring greens)
2 small organic eggs
2 fresh tomatoes (halved and cored)
Sea salt and freshly ground black pepper to taste

In a large wok or frying pan, heat the oil.
Add the garlic, leeks and spices. Stir-fry together with the chicken on a medium heat for about 10 - 15 minutes.
Wash the greens and add to the pan. Cook over a low heat and stir occasionally.
Add the tomato halves and simmer for about 15 minutes, or until the greens have broken down.
Pour in a little water, if needed, to prevent burning. Stir regularly.
In a small pan, boil the eggs in boiling water for 10 minutes, then place in a cold pan of water to cool down.
When you have peeled the shells, halve the eggs and add to the other ingredients.
Cook for a further couple of minutes until the eggs have warmed through.
Serve hot as it is, or with some brown rice.

# Chicken Soup

This is a perfect recipe for when you're feeling poorly, so it is probably worthwhile preparing some in readiness for the "Herxheimer Reaction" stage. As they say: "Chicken soup for the soul!"

**Serves 4**

*1 large knob of dairy and gluten-free spread*
*1 large organic chicken breast (with skin on)*
*1 medium leek (trimmed and sliced)*
*1 large onion (peeled and chopped)*
*¼ small swede (peeled and cubed)*
*1 large carrot (peeled and chopped)*
*2 stalks of celery (trimmed and sliced)*
*2 pints of vegetable stock*
*2 fresh bay leaves*
*½ pint of organic, unsweetened soya milk (optional)*
*Sea salt and freshly ground black pepper to taste*

Heat the spread in a large pan with a lid.
When melted, add the chicken breast whole with the skin on to create a bit more chicken stock flavour.
Fry on a medium heat for a couple of minutes on each side.
Add the leek and onion. Stir until they soften (about 5 minutes).
Add the swede, carrot and celery. Pour in the stock and bay leaves. Stir well.
Cover with the lid and simmer on a low heat for about 1 hour, stirring regularly.
Remove the bay leaves and throw them away.
Take out the chicken from the pan, remove the skin and discard it.
Chop up the chicken breast into bite-sized pieces and return the meat to the pan.
If you want to make the soup creamier, add the soya milk, warming through gently.
(Note that, if overheated, the soya milk goes frothy).
Alternatively, you can just blend with a hand-held blender until smooth.

# Chicken Stew

Chicken stew is a perfect meal for a winter's night in front of the telly! You can always use the left over meat from a roast chicken for this stew and use the carcass to make chicken stock.

**Serves 4 - 6**
*2 tablespoons of rapeseed oil*
*4 organic chicken thighs (with skin on)*
*1 large onion (peeled and chopped)*
*1 large leek (trimmed and sliced)*
*2 pints of boiling water (to make the chicken stock)*
*2 fresh bay leaves*
*2 large carrots (peeled and sliced)*
*1 large parsnip (peeled and diced)*
*1 small swede (peeled and cubed)*
*1 medium potato (peeled and chopped)*
*3 sticks of celery (trimmed and sliced chunkily)*
*115g (4oz) of green lentils and 115g (4oz) of red lentils*
*1 pint of stock*
*2 tablespoons of freshly chopped parsley*
*Sea salt and freshly ground black pepper to taste*

In a large cooking pot, heat the oil on a medium heat.
Wash the chicken thighs and add them to the oil, together with the onion and leek.
Fry for 2 - 3 minutes then stir in 2 pints of boiling water and add the bay leaves.
Simmer on a low heat for about 45 minutes (the chicken will practically fall off bone when done).
Take out the chicken, remove and dispose of the skin and bones. Return chicken meat to the stock.
Prepare the vegetables (chop them into any shape you like). Add them all at the same time.
Then pour in both colours of lentils and give it a good stir.
Add a further 1 pint of stock (homemade or made up with a yeast-free vegetable stock cube).
Simmer on a low heat for about an hour, stirring regularly to prevent burning at the bottom.
Add the parsley. Cook for a further 10 minutes. Remove the bay leaves.
Serve immediately, or freeze for lunches.

# Chicken
## with Mediterranean Lentils

You can't see it, but just off camera is my cat's head! I was taking this picture with one hand whilst trying to fend her off my chicken with the other!

**Serves 2**

*2 large organic chicken legs*
*1 tablespoon of extra virgin olive oil*
*1 handful of green beans (trimmed and chopped)*
*2 large cloves of garlic (peeled and chopped)*
*1 small red onion (peeled and chopped)*
*1 red pepper (cored, deseeded and sliced thinly)*
*225g (8oz) of red lentils*
*½ pint of vegetable stock*
*2 fresh bay leaves*
*10 black olives (sliced)*
*Sea salt and freshly ground black pepper to taste*

Preheat the oven to 180°C/350°F/gas mark 4.

Place the chicken leg on a roasting tray and drizzle with a little oil.

Cook this in the middle of the oven for 30 - 45 minutes.

When the skin is golden, check the chicken is cooked through. You may remove the skin if you wish.

In a steamer, or pan of boiling water, cook the green beans for 5 - 10 minutes until tender.

Drain the beans, but keep the stock from the beans to one side.

In a pan with a lid, heat the oil. Fry the garlic and onion on a medium heat until soft (about 5 minutes).

Add the pepper and cook for a further couple of minutes.

Pour in the lentils, stock and bay leaves. Stir thoroughly.

Simmer on a low heat for about 20 minutes, or until the lentils are cooked.

Add more water, if needed. Stir regularly.

Remove the bay leaves and mix in the olives and green beans.

Serve with the chicken and garnish with salad leaves.

# Chicken with Potato Salad
## and Red Cabbage & Pine Nut Salad

You really should remove the chicken skin, but I'm very naughty and have it as a little treat (we don't get many, let's face it!). Personally, I think it is the best bit of the chicken.

**Serves 4**

*4 organic chicken thighs (or drumsticks)*
*½ small red cabbage (sliced finely)*
*2 medium carrots (peeled and grated)*
*1 tablespoon of extra virgin olive oil*
*1 tablespoon of lemon juice*
*1 tablespoon of freshly chopped parsley*
*1 tablespoon of freshly chopped chives*
*½ teaspoon of freshly chopped marjoram (or dried)*
*2 tablespoons of pine nuts (toasted without oil)*
*3 large organic eggs*
*¼ small red onion (peeled and chopped)*
*500g (17½oz) of baby pearl potatoes (quartered)*
*1 tablespoon of extra virgin olive oil*
*Fresh chives*
*Sea salt and freshly ground black pepper to taste*

Preheat the oven to 190°C/375°F/gas mark 5.
Lay the chicken on a foil covered baking tray.
Season with pepper and sprinkle a little oil over the thighs.
Place in the middle of the oven and cook for about 30 minutes until cooked.
Serve with Potato Salad and Red Cabbage & Pine Nut Salad (see recipes).

# Chick Pea & Cherry Tomato Pasta

This is a relatively simple dish that you can make when you've had a tiring day at work and all you want to do is eat and sit down. You can also serve this cold as a pasta salad.

### Serves 4

*2 tablespoons of extra virgin olive oil*
*2 large cloves of garlic (peeled and chopped)*
*1 small red onion (peeled and chopped)*
*1 x 400g tin of chick peas (or 100g dried)*
*40 whole black olives*
*250g (8.8oz) vegetable rice pasta spirals*
*12 fresh cherry tomatoes (halved)*
*3 tablespoons of freshly chopped basil*
*Sea salt and freshly ground black pepper to taste*

If using tinned chick peas, drain them in a colander and rinse thoroughly with cold water and set aside.
If you are going to use dried peas, you will need less in weight as they expand in size as they rehydrate.
You will need to prepare 100g of dried peas per 400g tinned peas and soak them for the required time.
Follow the relevant instructions for cooking chick peas from dried. Tinned are so easy!
In a wok, heat the oil. Add the garlic and onion and fry gently on a medium heat.
Cook for about 5 minutes until soft, stirring regularly.
Put the chick peas and olives in the wok.
Turn off the heat until you are ready to add the cooked pasta.
In a very large pan, add about 4 litres (135 fl oz) of boiling water for every 250g (8.8oz) of pasta.
Stir gently and simmer on a medium heat for about 8 - 10 minutes until cooked, stirring regularly.
Drain the pasta into a colander and rinse well with boiling water.
Halve the cherry tomatoes and add them to the wok, together with the pasta and chopped basil.
Stir thoroughly on a low heat for a minute or two so that the tomatoes do not cook, but are just warm.
Serve whilst hot with a sprinkling of dairy-free Parmazano.

# Chinese Chicken with Noodles

If you are a vegetarian who eats fish, you can always substitute prawns for the chicken in this dish, or alternatively use tofu. I like to eat this meal with chopsticks for a bit of fun!

### Serves 3 - 4

*2 tablespoons of sunflower oil*
*3 large cloves of garlic (peeled and chopped)*
*1 tablespoon of sesame seeds*
*2 teaspoons of Chinese five spice*
*2 organic chicken thighs (or 1 small organic chicken breast)*
*1 stick of celery (trimmed and sliced)*
*8 radishes (trimmed and quartered)*
*6 spring onions (trimmed and chopped into 1 cm pieces)*
*½ red, yellow and green pepper (cored, deseeded and sliced)*
*400g (14oz) of bean sprouts*
*1 yeast-free vegetable stock cube*
*2 tablespoons of Bragg Liquid Aminos*
*125g (4.4oz) of organic corn and brown rice noodles*
*Freshly ground black pepper to taste*

Remove the skin and bone from the chicken thighs and dispose of this. Cut the meat into strips.
Heat the oil in a wok. Add the garlic, sesame seeds, Chinese five spice and chicken.
Fry on a medium heat for 3 - 4 minutes, stirring regularly. Add the celery, radish, spring onion and pepper.
Cover and cook on a low to medium heat for about 5 - 10 minutes, stirring frequently.
Mix the stock cube in ¼ pint of boiling water.
Add the bean sprouts, stock and Bragg Liquid Aminos to the wok and stir.
Cover with a lid and simmer for about 5 minutes, or until the vegetables are cooked to your taste.
In a large pan of boiling water, cook the noodles as per the pack instructions.
In a colander, drain the noodles.
Serve the noodles in a separate bowl, sprinkled with toasted sesame seeds and chopped coriander.
If you wish, you can add more Bragg Liquid Aminos to taste.

# Cod & Courgette Bean Salad

Scrummy! This is such a healthy meal you can't help but feel good after eating it. This can be turned into a vegetarian option by replacing the cod with chick peas.

### Serves 2
*2 chunky cod fillets (boneless and skinless)*
*16 cherry tomatoes*
*3 small cloves of garlic (peeled and roughly chopped)*
*2 tablespoons of extra virgin olive oil*
*2 small courgettes (trimmed and sliced)*
*1 red pepper (cored, deseeded and sliced)*
*1 x 400g tin of cannellini beans (or 100g dried)*
*¼ small red onion (peeled and chopped finely)*
*2 tablespoon of freshly chopped basil*
*Sea salt and freshly ground black pepper to taste*

If using tinned beans, drain them in a colander and rinse thoroughly with cold water and set aside.
If you are going to use dried beans, you will need less in weight as they expand in size as they rehydrate.
You will need to prepare 100g of dried beans per 400g tinned beans and soak them for the required time.
Follow the relevant instructions for cooking the particular types of beans from dried. Tinned are so easy!
Preheat the oven to 200°C/400°F/gas mark 6.
Put the cod on a large piece of foil, drizzle with a little oil. Wrap it up like a parcel.
Cook on a high shelf for about 30 - 35 minutes (frozen) and about 20 - 25 minutes (fresh).
(Open foil 10 minutes before the end of cooking time to dry off some of the moisture).
On a baking tray, lay out the cherry tomatoes, sprinkle over the chopped garlic.
Drizzle with 1 tablespoon of oil. Roast the tomatoes on a high shelf next to the cod for 10 minutes.
In a griddle pan, heat 1 tablespoon of oil. Lay the courgettes flat. Fry on a medium heat, turn when striped.
Griddle the pepper separately in the pan for about 5 minutes until cooked.
Pour the beans into a large salad bowl.
Add the cooked courgettes, peppers, cherry tomatoes, basil and onion to the beans.
Toss thoroughly then serve the cod immediately on top of the courgette bean salad.
Use any left over oil from the tomatoes and courgettes to pour over the cod, beans and vegetables.

# Coleslaw

Coleslaw is best eaten within 24 hours, so you can halve the measurements if you are just making it for yourself.  You can also make a Potato Salad with any excess Mayonnaise the following day.

**Serves 2 - 3**

*¼ small white cabbage (shredded finely)*
*1 medium carrot (peeled and grated)*
*½ small red onion (peeled and sliced finely)*
*2 - 3 tablespoons of homemade Mayonnaise (see recipe)*
*Sea salt and freshly ground black pepper to taste*

Slice the white cabbage very thinly and add to a large mixing bowl.
Grate the carrot and thinly slice the onion and add to the cabbage.
You can use as much or as less onion to your own taste as you want.
Add the amount of Mayonnaise (see recipe) you require to get the right consistency.
Toss the mixture so that the mayonnaise is evenly distributed.
Cover with cling film and place in the fridge until you are ready to serve it.

# Courgette & Butternut Squash Pasta

This recipe really surprised me when I first made it. I think it is because of the combination of the caramelised squash with the garlic and crunch of the pine nuts. It is delicious hot or cold. Tuck in!

**Serves 2 - 3**

*1 large butternut squash (peeled, deseeded and cubed)*
*2 large cloves of garlic (peeled and chopped)*
*2 - 3 tablespoons of extra virgin olive oil*
*1 large courgette (trimmed, sliced and halved)*
*3 tablespoons of pine nuts (toasted without oil)*
*250g (8.8oz) of vegetable and rice pasta*
*½ unwaxed, organic lemon*
*Sea salt and freshly ground black pepper to taste*

Preheat the oven to 200°C/400°F/gas mark 6.

Quarter the butternut squash, remove the skin and seeds and dispose of these. Chop the squash into small cubes.

On a baking tray covered with foil, sprinkle on the squash and garlic.

Drizzle 2 tablespoons of oil over the squash and stir thoroughly to coat.

Cover with foil and cook for 15 minutes. After this time, remove the foil.

Put the squash back in the oven for a further 30 minutes, or until slightly crispy and caramelised.

In a wok, gently fry the courgettes in a little oil, so that they still have some bite to them.

In a small frying pan on a low heat, dry toast the pine nuts (without oil) until just golden.

In a very large pan, add about 4 litres (135 fl oz) of boiling water for every 250g (8.8oz) of pasta.

Stir gently and simmer on a medium heat for about 8 - 10 minutes until cooked.

Drain the pasta into a colander and rinse well with boiling water.

In a large salad bowl, add the pasta, courgette, squash and pine nuts.

Squeeze the half of lemon over the mixture and a tiny drizzle of olive oil.

Toss thoroughly with salad servers and serve immediately.

# Creamy Celery Soup

You may find that soups will seem bland whilst your taste buds are adapting to their new lifestyle of less or no salt. Therefore, I would suggest just adding a clove of garlic to spice them up a bit.

**Serves 4**

*1 large knob of dairy and gluten-free spread*
*1 large onion (peeled and chopped)*
*1 large leek (trimmed and sliced)*
*1 small potato (peeled and cubed)*
*2 small carrots (peeled and cubed)*
*10 sticks of celery (trimmed and sliced)*
*1 pint of vegetable stock*
*2 fresh bay leaves*
*½ pint of organic, unsweetened soya milk*
*Organic corn cakes*
*Dairy and gluten-free spread*
*Sea salt and freshly ground black pepper to taste*

Melt the spread in a large pan on the stove.
Add the onion and leek. Stir on a medium heat for about 5 minutes until they soften.
Add the potato, carrot and celery. Mix well and then add the vegetable stock.
Simmer for 30 minutes or until the vegetables are cooked. Stir regularly.
Remove the bay leaves.
Add the soya milk, warming through gently (if overheated the soya milk goes frothy).
Blend with a hand-held blender.
Serve with organic corn cakes or rice cakes, with some dairy and gluten-free spread.

# Crispy Herbed Potatoes

If you are avoiding potatoes … sorry to tempt you with this delicious recipe! As an alternative to rosemary, try using different herbs, such as fresh basil or thyme, or even add onion and garlic.

**Serves 4**

*500g (17½oz) of organic King Edward potatoes*
*2 tablespoons of extra virgin olive oil*
*1 - 2 tablespoons of freshly chopped rosemary*
*Sea salt and freshly ground black pepper to taste*

Preheat the oven to 220°C/425°F/gas mark 7.
Scrub the potatoes, but do not peel them. Cut them in half.
In the oven, place a large roasting tray with a little olive oil in it to heat.
In a large pan, boil the potatoes with their skin on until they are almost cooked.
Drain and leave to cool a little.
Remove the roasting tray from the oven and lay the potatoes on it.
Using a masher, crush the potatoes a little.
Scatter the chopped rosemary over the potatoes and drizzle 2 tablespoons of oil over them.
Toss the crushed potatoes in the oil until they are coated well.
Roast the potatoes on a high shelf in the oven for about 40 minutes, or until crispy.
Serve with a piece of salmon or just about whatever you fancy.

# Crunchy Veggie Stir-Fry

Okay, so it's not vegetables in black bean sauce, or sesame prawn toast, but hooray for a healthy Chinese meal without the MSG!

## Serves 3 - 4

2 tablespoons of rapeseed oil
1 medium onion (peeled and chopped)
2 spring onions (trimmed and sliced)
1 large carrot (peeled and sliced thinly diagonally)
175g (6oz) of baby corn
1 x 3 inch piece of fresh ginger (peeled and sliced into strips)
2 large cloves of garlic (peeled and chopped)
1 tablespoon of sesame seeds
2 sticks of celery (trimmed and sliced thinly)
1 red pepper (cored, deseeded and sliced)
350g (12oz) of bean sprouts
1 yeast-free vegetable stock cube
½ teaspoon of Chinese five spice
250g (8.8oz) of rice noodles
Bragg Liquid Aminos spray (about 5 squirts or to taste)
Freshly ground black pepper to taste

In a wok, add the oil and heat until very hot. Add the onions, spring onion, carrot and corn.
Stir-fry on a medium to high heat for a minute, taking care not to burn the vegetables.
Next put in the ginger, garlic and sesame seeds and cook for a further minute.
Add the celery, red pepper and bean sprouts. Cook for two minutes, stirring occasionally.
In a jug, make up the stock cube with ¼ pint of boiling water and add the Chinese five spice to it.
Pour the stock in the wok, cover with a lid and, on a low heat, simmer for about 10 - 15 minutes.
In a large pan of boiling water, cook the noodles as per the pack instructions.
Add the noodles to the wok when cooked.
Warm through and serve.
Spray with Bragg Liquid Aminos to taste.

# Egg Fried Rice

You can also add some organic chicken meat and petit pois to this dish if you wish to bulk it out a bit and add more colour to it.

**Serves 2 - 3**

*225g (8oz) of brown basmati rice*
*1 teaspoon of turmeric*
*2 tablespoons of sunflower oil*
*3 large cloves of garlic (peeled and crushed)*
*1 level tablespoon of sesame seeds*
*6 spring onions (trimmed and chopped)*
*1 small carrot (peeled and cut julienne)*
*Bragg Liquid Aminos spray*
*3 large organic eggs*
*Freshly ground black pepper to taste*

In a large pan with a lid, pour in about 1½ pints of boiling water, a small drop of oil and the turmeric.
In a sieve, add the rice and rinse well with cold water then add the rice to the pan.
Cover and simmer on a low heat, stirring occasionally, for about 25 - 30 minutes until cooked.
In a colander, drain the cooked rice then rinse well with boiling water until the water runs clear.
Heat the oil in a wok.  Add the garlic, sesame seeds, spring onion and carrot.  Cook until softened.
Add 10 squirts of  Bragg Liquid Aminos spray.
Beat the 3 eggs in a bowl then add to the vegetables in the wok.
Stir the mixture as if making scrambled egg.
Add the rice and warm through.
Add more squirts of Bragg Liquid Aminos spray to taste.
Serve in a bowl and sprinkle some more sesame seeds on top.
Eat with chopsticks for a bit of fun!

# Fish Pie

This fish pie is delicious served with Asian Vegetable Salad (see recipe). As an alternative to cod, you can also try it with haddock, salmon or monkfish.

## Serves 4

*8 medium potatoes (peeled and quartered)*
*2 large organic eggs*
*1 large knob of dairy and gluten-free spread*
*2 meaty cod fillets (skinless and boneless)*
*250g (8.8oz) of king prawns (deveined and washed)*
*85g (3oz) of petit pois*
*200ml of coconut milk*
*Sea salt and freshly ground black pepper to taste*

Boil the potatoes for about 20 minutes until just cooked (to prevent them from turning starchy).
Preheat the oven to 180°C/350°F/gas mark 4.
Cook the eggs in a pan of boiling water for 10 minutes. When cool, remove shell and chop the egg.
Put the prawns in a colander, devein them then rinse with cold water and drain.
Heat the spread in a large frying pan. Fry the cod on a medium heat for about 5 - 10 minutes until flaky.
(Note that if the fish has skin, cook skin side down first if you want to remove this easily).
If you do not want to fry the fish, you can bake it in foil in the oven instead, for about 20 - 25 minutes.
Add the petit pois, prawns and coconut milk and simmer for 5 - 10 minutes.
If the sauce is too runny, boil it briefly until some of the water evaporates from it. Keep stirring.
Place the fish mixture in a flat ovenproof dish. Look out for any bones and remove them. Add the egg.
Drain the cooked potatoes and mash with a knob of spread until a thick, creamy consistency.
Spoon the mashed potato on top of the fish mixture making sure it doesn't leak over the side.
Flatten the mash potato down gently then run a fork over it to give it a textured appearance.
Bake it in the oven for about 15 minutes, or until heated through.

# Friday Night Mish Mash

This is an example of a meal which you can cook at the end of your working week from whatever vegetables you have left over in your fridge when your cupboards are bare. Voila!

**Serves 1**

*2 tablespoons of rapeseed oil*
*2 small cloves of garlic (peeled and chopped)*
*1 small red onion (peeled and chopped)*
*½ medium courgette (trimmed and cubed)*
*50g (1¾oz) of fresh spinach (washed)*
*1 stick of celery (trimmed and sliced)*
*1 x 150g tin of sweet corn and peppers*
*16 cherry tomatoes (halved)*
*1 small handful of freshly chopped basil*
*1 pack of ready-made polenta (or homemade)*
*1 large organic egg*
*Sea salt and freshly ground black pepper to taste*

In a wok, heat 1 tablespoon of oil.
Add the garlic, onion and courgette. Cook on a medium heat for 3 - 4 minutes.
Put in the spinach, celery and sweet corn.
Cook for a further couple of minutes until the spinach has broken down.
Add the basil and cherry tomatoes and warm through for a couple of minutes.
In a pan of boiling water, boil the egg for 5 minutes so that it is almost soft boiled. Cool and remove shell.
In a separate frying pan, heat 1 tablespoon of oil.
Slice up amount of polenta required and add to the pan.
Stir continuously until it is a similar consistency to mashed potato.
Serve the polenta on a plate, add the vegetable mixture and finally halve the egg on top of that.
Garnish with fresh chives.

# Fried Egg, Potato Cake & Tomato

A perfect idea for breakfast when you've made too much mashed potato the night before. You can make it even more exciting with a bit of onion or herbs thrown in!

### Serves 1
*1 tablespoon of sunflower oil*
*Left over mashed potato*
*1 medium tomato (halved)*
*1 large organic egg*
*Sea salt and freshly ground black pepper to taste*

In a large frying pan, heat the oil.
Using about 1 heaped tablespoon of mash per potato cake, flatten into a flat pattie shape.
Add the potato cake to the frying pan.
Cook on a medium heat for a couple of minutes on each side so it browns
Add the tomato to the side of the pan to warm through.
If frying, add the egg to the pan to cook to your liking (add more oil, if necessary).
Otherwise, poach or boil the egg if you would prefer.
Serve the egg sunny side up and eat immediately.

# Greedy Guts Salad

This is the ultimate salad to fill you up.  It is also nicer if you eat this as soon as you have cooked the courgette and pepper, so that it is still warm.

**Serves 4**
*1 romaine lettuce (trimmed and chopped)*
*85g (3oz) of fresh watercress (washed)*
*8 cherry tomatoes (halved)*
*¼ cucumber (sliced and quartered)*
*4 spring onions (trimmed and chopped)*
*1 x 400g tin of chick peas (or 100g dried)*
*1 tablespoon of rapeseed oil*
*1 medium courgette (trimmed and sliced)*
*1 orange pepper (cored, deseeded and sliced into rings)*
*1 teaspoon of extra virgin olive oil (or avocado oil)*
*1½ tablespoons of fresh lemon juice*
*5 teaspoons of tahini and 5 teaspoons of water*
*1 small clove of garlic (peeled and crushed)*
*1 tablespoon of pumpkin seeds*
*Sea salt and freshly ground black pepper to taste*

If using tinned chick peas, drain them in a colander and rinse thoroughly with cold water and set aside.
If you are going to use dried peas, you will need less in weight as they expand in size as they rehydrate.
You will need to prepare 100g of dried peas per 400g tinned peas and soak them for the required time.
Follow the relevant instructions for cooking the chick peas from dried.  Tinned are so easy!
In a large salad bowl, toss in the lettuce, watercress, tomatoes, cucumber, spring onions and chick peas.
In a griddle pan, add 1 tablespoon of oil and heat.  Lay the courgette slices in the pan.
Fry on a medium heat for 2 minutes each side, without moving them, until both sides have golden stripes.
Remove and add to salad, then fry the pepper rings on both sides until cooked.  Add these to the salad also.
In a salad dressing shaker, add the oil, lemon juice, tahini, water, garlic.
Shake well until mixed.  Taste a bit of the dressing to see if you need to add more of something.
Drizzle the required amount of dressing over the salad and sprinkle with pumpkin seeds.

# Guacamole Dip
## with Tortilla Chips

Shame about the Margueritas … but at least we can eat this! You can always leave out the cayenne pepper if you cannot tolerate the spice.

### Serves 2

*1 ripe avocado (peeled, de-stoned and mashed)*
*6 cherry tomatoes (quartered)*
*2 small cloves of garlic (peeled and crushed)*
*Small pinch of sea salt*
*½ teaspoon of black pepper (crushed)*
*¼ teaspoon of cumin seeds (crushed)*
*1 tablespoon of extra virgin olive oil*
*½ tablespoon of fresh lemon juice*
*Small pinch of cayenne pepper (optional)*
*1 small bag of unsalted or lightly salted tortilla chips*

Peel and de-stone the avocado, then mash with the chopped tomato in a large bowl.

In a mortar and pestle, pound the garlic, salt, pepper and cumin seeds.

Add this to the avocado and tomato mixture, then mix together with the oil and lemon juice.

Add a pinch of cayenne pepper and stir.

Cover and place in the fridge to cool.

Serve with tortilla chips

# Hummus

You can alter this recipe a number of ways by either adding 1 tablespoon of fresh coriander, or sun-dried tomatoes.  Try some different spices too (e.g. ground cumin or coriander).  Go on, experiment!

### Serves 4 - 6

*1 x 400g tin of chick peas (or 100g dried))*
*2 large cloves of garlic (peeled and chopped)*
*1 tablespoon of fresh lemon juice*
*1 tablespoon of tahini*
*2 tablespoons of extra virgin olive oil*
*Small pinch of sea salt*
*1 teaspoon of sesame seeds (toasted without oil)*

If using dried chick peas, wash them and put them in a large bowl.
Add enough water so that there is at least 2 inches of water above the chick peas.  Soak overnight in the fridge.
The next day, using a large saucepan boil the chick peas using the water they were soaked in.
Add a further 1 - 2 cups of water.  Bring to the boil. They can take anything up to 2 hours to soften.
Check the chick peas regularly and add more water if they need it.  Drain and set aside.
Alternatively, you can use a tin of ready-cooked chick peas to save a lot of time!
Put the chick peas into a blender, with the garlic, lemon juice, tahini and oil.  Blend to a smooth paste.
If the hummus is too thick, add a tablespoon of water at a time to get the right consistency.
Serve in a dish, pool a little oil in the centre and sprinkle with the toasted sesame seeds.
If you don't want to make a huge amount of hummus, then just halve the ingredients above.

# Hungarian Aubergine
## with Polenta

Beware of paprika! It can range from mild to very hot. Do a taste-test first and if it feels like chilli on your tongue find a mild variety. The last time I cooked this dish, I didn't, and it nearly took my face off!!

**Serves 3 - 4**

*1 small aubergine (trimmed and sliced)*
*2 tablespoons of sunflower oil*
*3 large cloves of garlic (peeled and chopped)*
*1 large red onion (peeled and diced)*
*1 orange pepper (cored, deseeded and diced)*
*1 large courgette (trimmed and diced)*
*2 sticks of celery (trimmed and diced)*
*1 yeast-free vegetable stock cube*
*4 fresh tomatoes (peeled, cored and chopped)*
*3 - 4 tablespoons of tomato purée*
*2 tablespoons of mild paprika*
*1 pack of ready-made polenta (or homemade)*
*Sea salt and freshly ground black pepper to taste*

Prepare the aubergine by trimming both ends off and slicing it into 1cm thick slices.
Spread the slices out onto a large plate and sprinkle liberally with a little sea salt on both sides.
Leave to sit for 20 minutes. Wash off the salt well with cold water and pat dry with kitchen towel.
This process removes much of the bitterness and can reduce fat absorption. Cut the aubergine into cubes.
Heat the oil in a wok or large saucepan with a lid.
Add about two-thirds of the garlic and all of the onion. Cook for about 5 minutes.
Then add the pepper, courgette, celery and aubergine. Stir-fry for a couple of minutes.
In a jug, make up the stock cube with ¾ pint of boiling water and pour in the pan.
Add the tomatoes, tomato purée, paprika and rest of the raw garlic.
Cover and simmer for about 45 minutes.
Slice the amount of polenta required into thin strips and then chop up smaller again.
Heat 2 tablespoons of oil in a large frying pan.
Add the polenta and stir continuously until it is a similar consistency to mashed potato.

# Kedgeree

Breakfast is the hardest meal of the day to cater for when you have Candida, so here's a traditional Victorian breakfast recipe for you.   It usually calls for smoked fish, but we have to stick to unsmoked.

### Serves 4
3 medium organic eggs
350g meaty cod fillets (skinless and boneless)
1 fresh bay leaf
1 yeast-free vegetable stock cube
225g (8oz) of brown basmati rice
1 large knob of dairy and gluten-free spread
1 large clove of garlic (peeled and crushed)
1 medium onion (peeled and chopped)
½ teaspoon of ground coriander and ½ teaspoon of turmeric
½ teaspoon of ground cumin and ½ teaspoon of fenugreek
½ teaspoon of poppy seeds and ½ teaspoon of mustard seeds
115g (4oz) of petit pois
1 tablespoon of fresh lemon juice
Sea salt and freshly ground black pepper to taste

In a pan of boiling water, cook the eggs for 10 minutes.  Drain, cool then remove shells and chop the egg.
In a large pan with a lid, lay the cod fillets and the bay leaf on the bottom.
In a jug, make up the stock cube with 1½ pints of boiling water then pour over the fish so it is covered.
Cover with the lid and simmer for about 10 minutes until the fish is cooked then remove the bay leaf.
Take the cod out of the stock with a slotted spoon and set it aside in a bowl to flake for use later.
In a sieve, add the rice.  Rinse well with cold water then add the rice to the pan containing the fish stock.
Cover and simmer on a low heat, stirring occasionally.  Cook for about 25 - 30 minutes until rice is cooked.
Brown rice is temperamental, so you can remove the lid at the end so any excess water can evaporate.
Alternatively, you can pour in a little more boiling water, if necessary, to cook the rice for longer until done.
In a wok or separate pan, heat the spread.  Add the onion and garlic.  Stir-fry on a low heat for 5 minutes.
Stir in the spices, seeds, petit pois and lemon juice.  Then add this together with the fish and the egg to the pan.
Warm through and garnish with a sprinkling of freshly chopped chives.

# King Prawn Indian Lemon Rice

If you do not eat fish, you can always substitute the prawns with a pulse of your choice instead. It will be just as tasty.

**Serves 3 - 4**

*225g (8oz) of brown basmati rice*
*1 teaspoon of turmeric*
*2 tablespoons of sunflower oil*
*2 - 3 teaspoons of cumin seeds*
*1 large red onion (peeled and diced)*
*3 large cloves of garlic (peeled and crushed)*
*Zest from 1 unwaxed, organic lemon (grated finely)*
*250g (8.8oz) of king prawns (deveined and washed)*
*2 fresh tomatoes (peeled, cored and chopped)*
*2 tablespoons of freshly chopped coriander*
*85g (3oz) of petit pois*
*2 tablespoons of fresh lemon juice*
*Sea salt and freshly ground black pepper to taste*

In a large pan with a lid, pour in about 1½ pints of boiling water, a small drop of oil and the turmeric.
In a sieve, add the rice and rinse well with cold water then add the rice to the pan.
Cover and simmer on a low heat, stirring occasionally, for about 25 - 30 minutes until cooked.
In a colander, drain the cooked rice then rinse well with boiling water until the water runs clear.
When cooked, rinse in a colander with boiling water to prevent stodginess, drain and set aside.
Put the prawns in a colander, devein them then rinse with cold water and drain.
Heat the oil in a wok. Add the cumin, onion, garlic and lemon zest.
Cook until the onion is soft (about 5 minutes).
Add the prawns, tomatoes, coriander and petit pois.
Cook until the prawns are done (about 5 - 10 minutes).
Add the rice and lemon juice to the wok.
Heat through and serve.

# King Prawns
## in Garlic & Parsley 'Butter'

This is a great pre-dinner snack when you have friends over for a meal. Alternatively, you can liven up any salad by tossing in these prawns.

**Serves 2 - 3**

*1 large knob of dairy and gluten-free spread*
*1 large clove of garlic (peeled and chopped)*
*250g (8.8oz) of king prawns (deveined and washed)*
*1 tablespoon of freshly chopped parsley*
*¼ fresh lemon*
*Freshly ground black pepper to taste*


Put the prawns in a colander, devein them then rinse with cold water and drain.

In a large frying pan, melt the spread.

Add the garlic and prawns and fry on a high heat for about 2 - 3 minutes.

Do not overcook the prawns as they shrink and become tough. You just want to warm them through.

If you are using raw prawns (these are grey in colour) cook them for a bit longer until they are pink all over.

Serve in a bowl and squeeze over some fresh lemon juice and sprinkle with a pinch of black pepper.

# King Prawn Skewers
## with Noodle Salad

These prawn skewers are delicious on their own as a snack, or as a first course appetizer. You can also experiment with different marinades for the prawns for other meals.

### Serves 2

250g (8.8oz) of king prawns (deveined and washed)
1 - 2 tablespoons of extra virgin olive oil
6 teaspoons of fresh lemon juice
2 large cloves of garlic (peeled and crushed)
½ teaspoon of mild paprika
½ teaspoon of turmeric
¼ teaspoon of cayenne pepper (optional)
2 teaspoons of freshly chopped root ginger
3 teaspoons of sesame seeds
1 medium carrot (peeled and cut into thin sticks)
3 spring onions (trimmed and sliced thinly)
1 handful of sugar snap peas
125g (4.4oz) of organic black rice noodles
¼ cucumber (cut into thin sticks)
4 squirts of Bragg Liquid Aminos spray
Freshly ground black pepper to taste

In a colander, devein the prawns and rinse them with cold water. Pat dry with some kitchen towel.
Place in a bowl. Add the oil, lemon juice, garlic, spices and ginger.
Stir well, cover and place in the fridge for 30 minutes to marinate.
Remove the prawns from the marinade and thread onto skewers.
In a wok, toast the sesame seeds then pour in the left over marinade from the prawns.
Add the carrot, spring onion and sugar snap peas. Stir-fry on a medium heat for 10 - 15 minutes.
In a large pan of boiling water, cook the noodles as per the pack instructions.
Place the prawn skewers on an oven tray and grill for about 5 - 6 minutes, turning once.
Add the cooked noodles and cucumber to the wok. Spray with Bragg Liquid Aminos and stir in. Warm through.
Serve noodles onto a plate and place prawn skewers on top. Decorate with lemon wedges.

# Lamb & Vegetables
## with Quinoa

The beauty of this dish is that it may be frozen and is actually tastier when reheated. If you are a vegetarian, you can omit the lamb, increase the amount of vegetables and add chick peas instead.

### Serves 3 - 4

*1 small aubergine (trimmed and sliced)*
*1 tablespoon of extra virgin olive oil*
*3 heaped teaspoons of ground cumin*
*3 heaped teaspoons of ground coriander*
*2 organic lamb chump chops (cubed)*
*1 large onion (peeled and chopped)*
*1 medium courgette (trimmed and sliced)*
*1 red pepper (cored, deseeded and chopped)*
*2 x 400g tins of tomatoes (or 8 fresh peeled tomatoes)*
*1 - 2 tablespoons of tomato purée*
*1 yeast-free vegetable stock cube*
*225g (8oz) of quinoa*
*Sea salt and freshly ground black pepper to taste*

Prepare the aubergine by slicing it and rubbing liberally with a little sea salt all over each side.
Leave to sit for 20 minutes. Wash off the salt well with cold water and pat dry with kitchen towel.
This process removes much of the bitterness and can reduce fat absorption. You can choose not to do this.
In a large pan, heat the oil and spices on a medium heat.
Put in the lamb and stir-fry for a couple of minutes to seal the meat, then remove from the pan.
Stir-fry the onion for about 5 minutes until soft. You can add also 1 - 2 tablespoons of water, if it needs it.
Add the courgette and pepper. Stir well. Pour in the tomatoes and tomato purée.
In a jug, make up the stock cube with ½ pint of boiling water. Pour in the stock and return lamb to the pan.
In a sieve, rinse the quinoa with cold water and drain. In a wok, toast the quinoa on a low heat for a minute.
Add 1 pint of boiling water to the quinoa and stir well. Cover with a lid.
Simmer on a low heat for about 15 minutes, stirring often until all the water is absorbed.
(Note that the grain will turn from white to transparent and the spiral-like tail will appear when it is cooked).
Serve the lamb dish with the quinoa and sprinkle with fresh coriander to garnish.

# Lamb Paprika Stew

You can eat this stew as it is, or you can also serve it with brown basmati rice and some delicious runner beans from your garden, or allotment.

## Serves 4

*2 tablespoons of extra virgin olive oil*
*3 large cloves of garlic (peeled and chopped)*
*4 organic lamb chump chops*
*2 medium onions (peeled and chopped chunkily)*
*3 medium leeks (trimmed and sliced chunkily)*
*2 tablespoons of mild paprika*
*2 medium carrots (peeled and sliced chunkily)*
*2 medium courgettes (trimmed, halved and sliced)*
*1 green pepper (cored, deseeded and diced)*
*1 small potato (peeled and cubed)*
*1 small aubergine (trimmed and sliced)*
*2 x 400g tins of tomatoes (or 8 fresh peeled tomatoes)*
*1 yeast-free vegetable stock cube*
*1 - 2 tablespoons of tomato purée*
*Sea salt and freshly ground black pepper to taste*

In a very large saucepan with a lid, heat the oil. Add the garlic and lamb.
Brown the lamb on all sides for a couple of minutes, but do not overcook.
Put in the onion and leek and stir-fry on a medium heat for about 5 minutes until they have softened.
Add the paprika and the rest of the vegetables, including the tomatoes. Mix thoroughly.
In a jug, make up the stock cube with 1 pint of boiling water.
Pour in the stock and add a further 2 pints of water, or as much as is needed to cover the vegetables.
Cover with the lid and simmer on a low heat for about an hour, stirring regularly.
When the meat is tender and the vegetables have cooked, add the tomato purée to thicken the sauce.

# Lambs' Lettuce Salad

You are going to be eating a lot of salad whilst you are on this diet, either as a main course, or as a side dish. This particular salad goes really well with my Pesto Cod recipe.

## Serves 2 - 3
*1 tablespoon of extra virgin olive oil*
*1 yellow pepper (halved, cored and deseeded)*
*100g (3½oz) of lambs' lettuce*
*5 large radishes (trimmed and sliced)*
*¼ cucumber (sliced)*
*2 tablespoons of pine nuts (toasted without oil)*
*Sea salt and freshly ground black pepper to taste*

Preheat the oven to 180°C/350°F/gas mark 4.
Cover a baking tray with foil. Cut the pepper in half and destalk it.
Drizzle with a little oil and sprinkle with a little salt and pepper. Bake in the oven for 15 - 20 minutes.
In a large salad bowl, add the washed lambs' lettuce, radishes and cucumber.
In a small frying pan on a low heat, dry toast the pine nuts (without oil) until just golden.
When the pepper is cooked, wait for it to cool a little and remove the skin (or leave, if preferred).
(You could always have raw pepper in the salad instead, if you don't have time to roast it).
Add the sliced pepper and toasted pine nuts to the salad.
Toss evenly.

# Lamb with Lentils

I love this dish for the rich flavours. It is a very tasty meal, as the lamb really soaks up the flavour of the cinnamon and garlic.

## Serves 3 - 4

*2 tablespoons of extra virgin olive oil*
*1 teaspoon of cumin seeds and ½ teaspoon of turmeric*
*1 x 3 inch stick of cinnamon*
*2 large cloves of garlic (peeled and chopped)*
*4 organic lamb chump chops*
*2 medium onions (peeled and chopped)*
*1 red pepper (cored, deseeded and chopped)*
*2 medium tomatoes (peeled, cored and chopped)*
*1½ pints of vegetable stock*
*100g (3½oz) of fresh spinach*
*85g (3oz) of red lentils*
*225g (8oz) of brown basmati rice*
*½ teaspoon of turmeric*
*Sea salt and freshly ground black pepper to taste*

Put the tomatoes in a bowl of boiling water for 5 minutes, so you can peel off the skin, then core and chop.
In a large saucepan with a lid, heat the oil.
Add the spices, garlic and lamb. Brown the meat for about 2 - 3 minutes.
Add the onion, pepper and tomato and stir-fry on a medium heat for a further couple of minutes.
Stir in the stock and lentils. Simmer with the lid on for 1 hour, stirring regularly, until the meat is tender.
About 15 minutes before the end of cooking, stir in the spinach and cook for a further 10 - 15 minutes.
Remove the cinnamon stick and discard.
In a separate large pan which has a lid, pour in 1½ pints of boiling water, a small drop of oil and the turmeric.
In a sieve, add the rice and rinse well with cold water then put the rice in the pan.
Cover and simmer on a low heat, stirring occasionally, for about 25 - 30 minutes until cooked.
In a colander, drain the cooked rice then rinse well with boiling water until the water runs clear.
Serve the lamb dish on a bed of rice.

# Lemon Quinoa
## with Chicken Kebabs

The use of quinoa in this dish makes it quite a light meal, as it is not as heavy duty as say brown rice. This would be good for a weekend lunch with the girls ... or boys!

### Serves 2

*2 tablespoons of extra virgin olive oil*
*½ teaspoon of freshly chopped oregano*
*1 large clove of garlic (peeled and crushed)*
*Grated rind and juice of 1 unwaxed, organic lemon*
*2 small organic chicken breasts (cut into 12 pieces)*
*½ red pepper (cored, deseeded and quartered)*
*½ green pepper (cored, deseeded and quartered)*
*6 cherry tomatoes*
*1 small red onion (peeled and quartered)*
*140g (5oz) of quinoa*
*1 yeast-free vegetable stock cube*
*6 sun-dried tomatoes (soaked and chopped)*
*1 tablespoon of freshly chopped basil*
*Sea salt and freshly ground black pepper to taste*

In a bowl, whisk together the oil, oregano, garlic and half of the lemon juice.

Add the cubed chicken, pepper, tomatoes and onion and toss to coat. Leave to marinate for 1 hour.

In a jug, make up the stock cube with about ¾ pint of boiling water.

In a sieve, rinse the quinoa with cold water and drain. In a wok, toast the quinoa on a low heat for a minute.

Add the stock to the quinoa and stir well. Cover with a lid.

Simmer on a low heat for about 15 minutes, stirring often until all the water is absorbed.

(Note that the grain will turn from white to transparent and the spiral-like tail will appear when it is cooked).

Preheat the grill. Thread the chicken cubes and pieces of vegetable alternately onto some skewers.

Place on a long baking tray covered in foil and use left over marinade to pour over the kebabs.

Grill about 3 - 4 inches from the heat for about 12 - 15 minutes on each side, turning once.

When the quinoa is ready, mix in the sun-dried tomatoes, basil and other half of the lemon juice and zest.

Serve the quinoa onto a plate and add the cooked kebab skewers on top.

# Marinated Tuna
## with Summer Roasted Vegetables

This dish started out as quite an experiment, as I had never really cooked fresh tuna before. However, my partner, Sam, gave this recipe the thumbs up!

### Serves 2

*Juice and flesh of 1 unwaxed, organic lemon*
*2 tablespoons of grated red onion*
*2 tablespoons of Bragg Liquid Aminos*
*1 - 2 teaspoons of extra virgin olive oil*
*2 teaspoons of freshly chopped thyme*
*2 fresh tuna steaks*
*1 medium courgette (trimmed and sliced)*
*1 red pepper (cored, deseeded and chopped)*
*1 yellow pepper (cored, deseeded and chopped)*
*1 medium leek (trimmed and sliced)*
*10 cherry tomatoes (whole)*
*2 large cloves of garlic (peeled and sliced)*
*1 - 2 tablespoons of extra virgin olive oil*
*2 tablespoons of freshly chopped basil*
*1 fresh corn cob*
*Freshly ground black pepper to taste*

Preheat the oven to 190°C/375°F/gas mark 5.
In a jug, combine the lemon juice, onion, Bragg Liquid Aminos, oil and thyme.
Lay the tuna steaks in a flat dish. Pour the mixture over them. Cover and chill in the fridge for 30 minutes.
In a large ovenproof dish, spread the vegetables and garlic equally.
Drizzle oil over the vegetables and sprinkle the basil over the top evenly.
Roast in the middle of the oven for about 40 minutes, or until just cooked.
Remove the tuna from the dish and put the rest of the marinade to one side for later.
Grill or griddle the fish for 5 minutes on each side, or until it is cooked the way you like it.
Place the tuna on a plate and add 1 tablespoon of the marinade on top of the fish.
Serve with the roasted vegetables and a freshly boiled corn cob (with a knob of spread on top).

# Mayonnaise

Hooray for this recipe, I cannot live without mayo! See my Coleslaw recipe. It will not taste the same as the mayonnaise you would normally have had, but you will soon get used to the new flavour.

**Makes approximately 5 - 6 tablespoons**
*1 large organic egg (use the yolk only)*
*2 - 4 teaspoons of fresh lemon juice to taste*
*Small pinch of sea salt*
*1 teaspoon of mustard seeds (crushed)*
*100ml (3½ fl oz) of extra virgin olive oil*
*½ tablespoon of boiling water*

In a mortar and pestle, add 1 teaspoon of mustard seeds. Crush to a fine powder (you do not use all of this).
Place a large glass or pottery mixing bowl in a sink of hot water to warm the bottom of it. Remove.
Break the egg and separate the yolk from the white. Put just the yolk into the warmed bowl.
Hand beat with a large wire whisk for about 2 minutes until the yolk is a thick consistency.
Do not scrimp on whisking - the more you whisk the better.
Add 1 teaspoon of lemon juice and a small pinch of salt and mustard powder. Beat for another 30 seconds.
You are now ready to introduce the oil. This is the hard part!
Make sure the oil is not too cold (room temperature is okay) and pour in about 1 teaspoon at a time.
Check that the egg yolk is absorbing the oil and that it is not curdling.
Do not stop beating until the sauce thickens. Two whisk strokes per second should be about right.
When you have used half the oil, the thickness should be cream-like.
Thin the mayo by adding 1 - 3 teaspoons of lemon juice if it gets too thick (or whatever it needs it for taste).
You can now add the oil by tablespoon amounts, but make sure it blends thoroughly.
Lastly, whisk the boiling water into the mayonnaise to prevent further curdling.
Place the mayonnaise into a dish and cover tightly with cling film to stop a skin forming.
(Note that you can always add a small clove of fresh crushed garlic to this as an alternative taste).
Refrigerate and use as soon as possible in a coleslaw or a potato salad.

# Meatballs & Spaghetti Sauce

This meal is so delicious that you'll forget you've got Candida until it comes to pudding, of course.
Grrrrr!  Life just isn't fair sometimes is it!

**Serves 2 - 3**

*2 tablespoons of extra virgin olive oil*
*2 large cloves of garlic (peeled and chopped)*
*8 medium fresh tomatoes (peeled, cored and chopped)*
*1 handful of fresh basil leaves*
*250g (8.8oz) of organic lamb mince*
*½ medium red onion (peeled and chopped finely)*
*2 tablespoons of freshly chopped parsley*
*1 small organic egg*
*2 tablespoons of polenta (maize flour)*
*200g (7oz) of corn spaghetti*
*Sea salt and freshly ground black pepper to taste*

In a medium sized pan, heat 1 tablespoon of oil and fry half of the garlic until soft, but do not burn it.
Add the tomatoes.  Simmer on a low heat for about 20 minutes (add a little water, if needed). Stir often.
Put in the basil and rest of the garlic and cook for a further 5 minutes.
Blend the sauce in a liquidiser, or with a hand-held blender, to a smooth paste and return to pan.
If you want to give the sauce a more intense flavour, you can add a few chopped sun-dried tomatoes.
In a large dish, place the mince, onion and parsley.  Break the egg on top.
Combine the ingredients with your hands.  When all is mixed in, shape into small walnut-sized balls.
If the mixture is not holding together too well, add a little bit of oil.
Shake some polenta onto a plate and coat each meatball in this to help hold their shape.
In a frying pan, heat about 1 - 2 tablespoons of oil.
Fry the meatballs in the pan until cooked through (about 15 minutes).
When the meatballs are done, add them to the sauce and simmer for a further 10 minutes.
Cook the spaghetti pasta as per the pack instructions of whichever brand you are using.
Serve the spaghetti, adding the meatballs and sauce on top.  Add some dairy-free Parmazano too, if you like.

# Millet & Tofu Scramble

Ever tried to get a four year old to eat asparagus? It may not be good table manners, but try pretending it is a snake's tongue ... they can't get a spear in their mouth quick enough!

### Serves 2

*115g (4oz) of yellow millet (rinsed and cooked)*
*1 yeast-free vegetable stock cube*
*1 tablespoon of rapeseed oil*
*2 large cloves of garlic (peeled and crushed)*
*1 large onion (peeled and chopped)*
*1 large courgette (trimmed and grated)*
*½ teaspoon of grated, unwaxed, organic lemon rind*
*1 tablespoon of Bragg Liquid Aminos*
*2 teaspoons each of pumpkin seeds and sunflower seeds*
*1 teaspoon each of poppy seeds and linseed*
*85g (3oz) of firm tofu (crumbled)*
*1 bunch of asparagus spears (base end trimmed)*
*Sea salt and freshly ground black pepper to taste*

In a sieve, rinse the millet with cold water and drain well.
In a saucepan with a lid, toast the millet on a low heat for a minute, stirring continuously.
In a jug, make up the stock cube with ¾ pint of boiling water. Pour in and stir well. Cover with lid.
Simmer on a low heat for about 20 minutes, stirring regularly, until cooked and all water is absorbed.
In a wok, heat the oil. Add the garlic and onion and cook for about 5 minutes until soft.
Add the courgette and stir for a further couple of minutes.
Put in the lemon rind, Bragg Liquid Aminos and seeds. Crumble the tofu into the wok. Stir well.
Heat the millet mixture through for a few more minutes until you are ready to serve.
In a griddle pan, gently cook the asparagus in a drizzle of extra virgin olive oil for about 5 - 10 minutes.
Serve the millet and asparagus with a dollop of Roasted Red Pepper and Garlic Pesto (see recipe).

# Minestrone Soup

Minestrone means "big soup" and this sure will fill you up!  The great thing about minestrone is that you can use whatever vegetables you have left over in your fridge.  Just throw it all in.

**Serves 4 - 5**
*2 tablespoons of sunflower oil*
*1 large onion (peeled and chopped)*
*2 large cloves of garlic (peeled and chopped)*
*1 medium potato (peeled and diced)*
*1 large carrot (peeled and diced)*
*1 large courgette (trimmed and diced)*
*2 sticks of celery (trimmed and chopped)*
*¼ white or sweetheart cabbage (chopped)*
*1 yeast-free vegetable stock cube*
*2 x 400g tins of tomatoes (or 8 fresh peeled tomatoes)*
*2 - 3 tablespoons of tomato purée*
*1 small handful of corn spaghetti*
*1 - 2 tablespoons of freshly chopped basil*
*Sea salt and freshly ground black pepper to taste*

In a large saucepan, heat the oil.
Add the onion and garlic (leave a little raw garlic aside to add just before the end).
Fry on a medium heat for about 5 minutes until the onion softens, stirring regularly.
Put in the potato, carrot, courgette, celery and cabbage.  Cook on a medium heat for about 5 - 7 minutes.
In a jug, make up the stock cube with 1½ pints of boiling water.  Pour in the stock and tomatoes and bring to the boil.
Reduce the heat and simmer for 30 - 40 minutes, stirring regularly.
Break up the spaghetti into short pieces and cook separately, as per pack instructions.  Drain and set aside.
Add the tomato purée to thicken the soup, as required.
Just before serving, add the pasta and the rest of the garlic to the soup.  Warm through.
Ladle into bowls and top each one with a sprinkling of dairy-free Parmazano and the basil to garnish

# Mixed Vegetables in Gravy

This is a quick and simple meal if you've not got much time to cook one evening. You don't have to stick with what vegetables I have used in this recipe. Use whatever you fancy.

## Serves 4

*2 tablespoons of rapeseed oil*
*3 large cloves of garlic (peeled and chopped)*
*1 small onion (peeled and sliced)*
*1 medium courgette (trimmed and sliced julienne)*
*1 medium carrot (peeled and sliced julienne)*
*1 handful of green beans (trimmed and chopped)*
*85g (3oz) of bean sprouts*
*Gluten-free vegetable gravy mix (made up with 200ml of boiling water)*
*Sea salt and freshly ground black pepper to taste*

In a wok, heat the oil.
Add the garlic and onion and fry gently on a medium heat until they have softened (about 5 minutes).
Stir in the courgette, carrot and green beans.
Cover with a lid and cook for about 10 minutes, stirring regularly.
In a measuring jug, add 200ml of boiling water.
Stir in the gravy mix 1 teaspoon at a time (you can make this as thick or as thin as you prefer it).
Alternatively, you can follow the pack instructions for how much gravy powder per 200ml of water.
Add the bean sprouts to the wok and stir thoroughly.
Replace the lid and cook for about 5 minutes until the vegetables have softened to your taste.
Don't overcook the vegetables; leave them with some bite.
Pour the gravy over the vegetables in the wok and heat through.
Make up a little more gravy, if you think it needs it.
Serve immediately.

# Nasi Goreng

This is the national dish of Indonesia, but I don't see why we can't enjoy it too! You can also liven it up with a couple of king prawn or chicken skewers, or some strips of stir-fried tofu.

**Serves 4**
*225g (8oz) of brown basmati rice*
*2 tablespoons of rapeseed oil*
*3 large cloves of garlic (peeled and crushed)*
*6 spring onions (trimmed and chopped)*
*1 heaped teaspoon of freshly chopped ginger*
*½ teaspoon of turmeric and ½ teaspoon of coriander*
*½ teaspoon of fenugreek and ½ teaspoon of ground cumin*
*1 teaspoon of poppy seeds*
*1 yellow pepper (cored, deseeded and diced)*
*2 small courgettes (trimmed and diced)*
*2 small carrots (peeled and diced)*
*½ small white or sweetheart cabbage (thinly sliced)*
*3 tablespoons of Bragg Liquid Aminos*
*4 medium organic eggs*
*Sea salt and freshly ground black pepper to taste*

In a large pan with a lid, pour in about 1½ pints of boiling water and a small drop of oil.
In a sieve, add the rice and rinse well with cold water, then add the rice to the pan.
Cover and simmer on a low heat, stirring occasionally, for about 25 - 30 minutes until cooked.
In a colander, drain the cooked rice then rinse well with boiling water until the water runs clear. Set aside.
In a wok, heat the oil. Add the garlic, spring onions, ginger, spices and poppy seeds.
Cook for 2 - 3 minutes, stirring gently. Add the pepper, courgette and carrot and fry for 2 - 3 more minutes.
Next put in the cabbage and stir-fry for a few minutes until the vegetables are done to your taste.
Pour in the Bragg Liquid Aminos and add the rice. Mix in thoroughly and heat through for a couple of minutes.
Serve the rice mixture on a bed of shredded, crispy lettuce with some sliced cucumber and tomato.
Prepare either a fried egg or an omelette, cut into strips (one egg per person) and lay on top of the rice.

# Onion Bhaji

This amount of mixture makes enough for four bhajis, so you may be doubling it up!  You can also try adding some fresh coriander to the mix to give it a bit of zing.

**Serves 4**
*2 tablespoons of rapeseed oil*
*2 large onions (peeled and sliced)*
*85g (3oz) of chick pea (gram) flour*
*½ teaspoon of turmeric*
*½ teaspoon of ground coriander*
*½ teaspoon of ground cumin*
*½ teaspoon of ground ginger*
*Small pinch of cayenne pepper (optional)*
*1 large teaspoon of tomato purée*
*2 tablespoons of boiling water*

Preheat the oven to 190°C/375°F/gas mark 5.
In a large wok or frying pan, heat 1 tablespoon of oil and add the onions.
Stir-fry the onions for about 10 - 15 minutes until they soften.  However, do not brown the onions.
(Note that the thinner you slice the onions, the quicker they will cook).
Add the spices to the pan.  Stir well for a minute or two then turn off the heat.
In a large mixing bowl, sieve in the flour.
Pour in the onions on top of the flour and mix thoroughly so that the onions are coated evenly.
In a small cup, mix together the tomato purée and water.
Add this to the bowl of onions and stir in well.
Lightly grease a baking tray with a little oil or spread.
Spoon the onion bhaji mixture separately into four round dollops onto the tray.
Place the tray containing the bhajis into the oven for 10 minutes.
Remove from the oven and drizzle the onion bhajis with the remaining 1 tablespoon of oil.
Place back into the oven for another 10 - 15 minutes or until golden and slightly crispy.

# Parsnip Soup

You could use soya milk in this recipe instead, but I think that the coconut milk gives this soup a richer flavour. You can also bulk out the soup a bit more by adding some red lentils to the recipe.

**Serves 4**

*1 large knob of dairy and gluten-free spread*
*1 large clove of garlic (peeled and chopped)*
*1 large onion (peeled and chopped)*
*1 large leek (trimmed and sliced)*
*2 large parsnips (peeled and cubed)*
*1 large carrot (peeled and cubed)*
*1 - 1½ pints of vegetable stock*
*100ml of coconut milk*
*Fresh flat leaf parsley to garnish*
*Sea salt and freshly ground black pepper to taste*

In a large cooking pot with a lid, melt the spread.
Add the garlic, onion and leek. Stir and cook on a medium heat until they soften (about 5 minutes).
Put in the parsnip, carrot and stock. Stir and cover with lid.
If needed, add more water to the pan to cover the vegetables.
Simmer for about 40 minutes, or however long it takes to cook the parsnip, stirring regularly.
Pour in the coconut milk and simmer for a further couple of minutes.
Use a hand-held food mixer to whizz down the mixture.
Garnish with a sprig of parsley.
Serve with rice cakes or corn cakes.

# Passata

Use high quality, ripe and organic tomatoes for this recipe. If you add ½ pint of organic unsweetened soya milk to this sauce, you've also got yourself a delicious tomato soup!

**Serves 4 - 6**

*2lb (32oz) of fresh medium tomatoes (halved and cored)*
*3 - 4 large cloves of garlic (peeled and chopped)*
*1 large onion (peeled and sliced)*
*2 tablespoons of extra virgin olive oil*
*1 heaped tablespoon of freshly chopped basil*
*Sea salt and freshly ground black pepper to taste*

Preheat the oven to 200°C/400°F/gas mark 6.
In a large baking tray, place the halved tomatoes (seed side up) next to each other.
Sprinkle over the onion and garlic. Drizzle with the oil.
Bake in the middle of the oven for about 1 hour.
Check on the tomatoes after about 20 minutes and stir so the onions do not burn.
When the tomatoes are cooked, leave to cool slightly before removing the skins and discarding them.
Transfer the contents of the roasting tray into a liquidiser/food processor.
Add the basil, together with a pinch of salt and pepper.
Whizz it up for a couple of minutes, so that it becomes a thick sauce.
About 10 medium to large-sized tomatoes will make approximately 800ml (27 fl oz) of tomato sauce.
This sauce can be used for so many different meals.

# Pesto Cod
## with Lambs' Lettuce Salad

This is a great meal for protein and greens for those of you avoiding carbohydrates. You can also use a different piece of fish for this recipe too. Why not try some lemon sole or haddock?

**Serves 2**

*2 meaty cod fillets (skinless and boneless)*
*100ml (3½ fl oz) of extra virgin olive oil*
*2 small cloves of garlic (peeled and chopped finely)*
*25g (1oz) of freshly chopped basil*
*50g (2oz) of pine nuts (toasted without oil)*
*1 tablespoon of fresh lemon juice*
*Dairy-free Parmazano*
*1 tablespoon of extra virgin olive oil*
*1 yellow pepper (halved, cored and deseeded)*
*100g (3½oz) of lambs' lettuce*
*5 large radishes (trimmed and sliced)*
*¼ cucumber (sliced)*
*2 tablespoons of pine nuts (toasted without oil)*
*Sea salt and freshly ground black pepper to taste*

Preheat the oven to 180°C/350°F/gas mark 4.
Wash, remove the skin and de-bone the fish, if needed.
Place the fish on a foil covered baking tray.
Drizzle 2 - 3 tablespoons of the Pesto Dressing (see recipe) over each loin.
Cover loosely with the foil and bake in the oven for about 15 - 20 minutes.
When the cod looks sufficiently cooked, open the foil.
Grill the top of the loins for a further 5 minutes, or until browned.
Serve with Lambs' Lettuce Salad (see recipe).
You can always use some Pesto Dressing on the salad too.
Eat whilst the fish is hot.

# Pesto Dressing

This dressing is great over some pasta, fish or salad for a quick and easy meal. Sprinkle over some dairy-free Parmazano for an authentic cheesy flavour.

**Makes approximately 5 - 6 tablespoons**
*100ml (3½ fl oz) of extra virgin olive oil*
*2 small cloves of garlic (peeled and chopped finely)*
*25g (1oz) of freshly chopped basil*
*50g (2oz) of pine nuts (toasted without oil)*
*1 tablespoon of fresh lemon juice*
*Sea salt and freshly ground black pepper to taste*
*Dairy-free parmazano*

In a small frying pan on a low heat, dry toast the pine nuts (without oil).
Stir regularly until they turn a lovely golden colour.
In a food processor or liquidiser, add the oil, garlic, basil and toasted pine nuts.
Add a small pinch of sea salt and freshly ground black pepper.
Whizz it up for a minute or two until it becomes a smooth thick purée.
This dressing will not stay fresh for longer than a day or two.
If you have some Pesto Dressing left over, you can always put it in a tub and freeze it for another day.

# Pork Casserole
## with Broccoli & Mash

You cannot beat mashed potato for comfort food on a dark and cold winter's evening. Obviously, don't go overboard; just have a dollop as a treat with the casserole and bulk up on green vegetables.

**Serves 3 - 4**

1 tablespoon of extra virgin olive oil
2 organic pork loin chops (cubed)
1 large clove of garlic (peeled and crushed)
1 medium onion (peeled and diced)
2 stalks of celery (trimmed and sliced)
2 small carrots (peeled and sliced)
1 medium courgette (trimmed, sliced and halved)
1 red pepper (cored, deseeded and chopped)
1 yellow pepper (cored, deseeded and chopped)
4 fresh medium tomatoes (peeled, cored and chopped)
1 yeast-free vegetable stock cube
2 tablespoons of tomato purée
1 teaspoon of freshly chopped thyme
1 tablespoon of freshly chopped parsley
Potatoes
Broccoli
Sea salt and freshly ground black pepper to taste

In a large pan with a lid, heat the oil. Add the pork and fry on a medium heat for about 3 - 4 minutes.
Add the garlic and onion and stir in with the meat for a couple more minutes.
Then stir in the celery, carrot, courgette, peppers and tomatoes.
In a jug, make up the stock cube with 1½ pints of boiling water (or you can use homemade stock).
Add the stock, tomato purée and herbs. Stir thoroughly.
Cover and simmer on a low heat for about 45 minutes until the meat falls apart.
Serve with a small dollop of potato (mashed with some spread and soya milk) and steamed broccoli.

# Potato Salad

This potato salad can be served hot with a piece of cooked salmon or organic lamb chop, but don't fill your plate with loads of potato. Remember we are keeping our carbohydrate intake as low as we can.

**Serves 4**

*3 large organic eggs*
*¼ small red onion (peeled and chopped)*
*500g (17½oz) of baby pearl potatoes (quartered)*
*1 tablespoon of extra virgin olive oil*
*Freshly chopped chives to garnish*
*Sea salt and freshly ground black pepper to taste*

In a pan of boiling water, add the potatoes.
Simmer for about 15 - 20 minutes until they are cooked (but not too soft and starchy).
In another pan of boiling water, cook the eggs for 10 minutes until hard boiled.
Empty the hot water from the egg pan and add some cold water for the eggs to cool in.
Chop up the onion finely.
When the eggs are cool, remove and discard their shells then chop the eggs into small chunks.
In a large salad bowl, add the potato, onion and chopped egg.
Spoon over the oil and mix in.
Garnish with some chopped chives.

# Prawn Curry

Again, if you are a vegetarian or vegan, you can always substitute the prawns in this dish for another vegetable or pulse, if you are not a fish eater.

## Serves 4

2 teaspoons of cumin seeds and 4 cardamom pods (crushed)
2 teaspoons each of Chinese five spice and ground coriander
1 x 3 inch stick of cinnamon
Small pinch of cayenne pepper (optional)
2 tablespoons of rapeseed oil
4 large cloves of garlic (peeled and chopped)
1 medium onion (peeled and chopped)
1 medium leek (trimmed and sliced)
2 sticks of celery (trimmed and sliced)
2 small courgettes (trimmed and cubed)
200g (7oz) of fresh prawns (washed)
1 x 400ml tin of coconut milk
1 tablespoon of tomato purée
Fresh coriander to garnish
Sea salt and freshly ground black pepper to taste

In a mortar and pestle, break up the cumin seeds a bit.
Crush the cardamom pods, so they open and the seeds are released (put it all in, but you don't eat the shell).
Heat a wok on a medium heat. Add all the spices and toast them, stirring occasionally, for about 5 minutes.
Next put in the oil, garlic, onion and leek (add a tablespoon of water to the wok, if you think it needs it).
In a colander, rinse the prawns with cold water and drain.
Stir for about 5 minutes until the onion softens, then add the celery, courgette and prawns.
Stir-fry for about 5 - 10 minutes. Pour in the coconut milk and tomato purée and mix in thoroughly.
Simmer with the lid off for about 10 minutes.
If the sauce needs thickening, cook on a high heat for a little bit, stirring regularly, to evaporate some milk off.
Serve with noodles (or brown basmati rice) and a sprinkling of fresh coriander to garnish.

# Quick & Easy King Prawn Spaghetti

When you do not have a lot of time on your hands, this is a relatively quick recipe, so that you can get out of the kitchen and go and do what you need to do!

**Serves 2 - 3**

*200g (7oz) of corn spaghetti*
*1 - 2 tablespoons of extra virgin olive oil*
*1 large clove of garlic (peeled and crushed)*
*1 medium red onion (peeled and chopped)*
*115g (4oz) of petit pois*
*250g (8.8oz) of king prawns (deveined and washed)*
*1 tablespoon of tomato purée*
*10 cherry tomatoes (halved)*
*1 tablespoon of freshly chopped parsley*

*Sea salt and freshly ground black pepper to taste*

Cook the spaghetti pasta as per the instructions of the particular brand you are using.
In a colander, rinse the spaghetti with boiling water, drain and leave to one side.
Put the prawns in a colander, devein them then rinse with cold water and drain.
In a wok, heat the oil and fry up the garlic and chopped onion on a medium heat for about 5 minutes.
When these have softened, add the petit pois and prawns, stirring regularly.
Cook for a couple of minutes until the prawns are cooked, but not overdone, as they become tough.
Add the tomato purée and 2 tablespoons of boiling water.
Halve the cherry tomatoes and put these in, together with the chopped parsley.
Add the cooked spaghetti to the wok and toss so it is coated in the tomato sauce.
Warm through and serve straightaway.

# Ratatouille

The larger the girth of the vegetables the easier it will be for you, as you won't need as many aubergines and courgettes to fill up your tray.

**Serves 4**

*1 pint (568ml) of Passata (see recipe)*
*2 tablespoons of extra virgin olive oil*
*2 medium courgettes (trimmed and sliced)*
*2 medium tomatoes (sliced)*
*2 small aubergines (trimmed and sliced)*
*1 orange pepper (cored, deseeded and sliced into rings)*
*Fresh basil leaves to garnish*
*Sea salt and freshly ground pepper to taste*

If you are using homemade passata, make sure you prepare this in advance (see recipe).
You can use a ready-made passata from a jar (but make sure it does not contain citric acid).
Preheat oven to 200°C/400°F/gas mark 6.
Slice the courgettes, tomatoes, aubergines and pepper into rounds about ¼ inch thick.
In a medium-sized, oven-proof dish, pour enough of the passata to cover the bottom.
Layer the vegetables alternately in rows or circles, depending on how you want it to look.
Place another layer of vegetables on top, so that they slightly overlap the ones below.
Continue to do this until you run out of vegetables, passata or bowl space.
Pour the remaining passata over the vegetables.
Bake in the middle of the oven for about an hour until the vegetables are cooked.
If you do not have an hour to spare, you can cook the ratatouille in a pan instead.
Heat the oil.  Stir-fry the vegetables for about 10 - 15 minutes until cooked.  Pour the passata over the top.
Garnish with basil and a sprinkling of dairy-free Parmazano.

# Red Cabbage & Pine Nut Salad

This recipe is a very simple, but effective, variation on a salad. It is really colourful and tasty and looks great on the table too!

**Serves 4**

½ small red cabbage (sliced finely)
2 medium carrots (peeled and grated)
1 tablespoon of extra virgin olive oil
1 tablespoon of lemon juice
1 tablespoon of freshly chopped parsley
1 tablespoon of freshly chopped chives
½ teaspoon of freshly chopped marjoram (or dried)
2 tablespoons of pine nuts (toasted without oil)
Sea salt and freshly ground black pepper to taste

Shred the cabbage into very thin slices. Grate the carrot.
Add to a large salad bowl.
Pour over the oil and lemon juice.
Sprinkle in the parsley, chives and marjoram.
In a small frying pan on a low heat, dry toast the pine nuts (without oil) until just golden.
Add to the bowl and mix thoroughly.

# Rhubarb & Spinach Curry

Well, I bet you weren't expecting that! Who'd have thought that you could actually have rhubarb without the custard! Isn't life full of surprises!

**Serves 4**

2 tablespoons of extra virgin olive oil
3 teaspoons of whole cumin seeds
1 teaspoon of ground coriander
½ teaspoon of ground cinnamon
½ teaspoon of turmeric
Small pinch of cayenne pepper (optional)
2 large cloves of garlic (peeled and chopped)
2 medium onions (peeled and chopped)
4 medium rhubarb stems (trimmed and sliced)
200g (7oz) of fresh spinach
1 yeast-free vegetable stock cube
85g (3oz) of red lentils
1 x 400g tin of gungo (pigeon) peas
Sea salt and freshly ground black pepper to taste

In a wok, heat the oil on a medium heat.
Add the spices, garlic and onion. Stir-fry on a medium heat for about 5 minutes until softened.
In a jug, make up the stock cube with 1 pint of boiling water.
Stir in the rhubarb, spinach, stock and lentils.
Simmer on a low heat for about 30 minutes, or until the vegetables are cooked, stirring regularly.
Add the gungo peas and warm through.
Serve with cooked brown basmati rice.

# Rice Cakes with Crab Topping

You can also use tinned tuna for this, of course, but I wanted to give you an unconventional substitute. This mixture can also be used as an alternative topping for a baked potato. Crab is very enjoyable.

**Serves 2**

*140g of fresh crab claw meat*
*6 radishes (trimmed and chopped finely)*
*¼ small red onion (peeled and chopped finely)*
*1 - 2 tablespoons of Hummus or Mayonnaise (see recipes)*
*Organic unsalted wholegrain rice cakes*
*Dairy and gluten-free spread*
*Fresh chives*
*Sea salt and freshly ground black pepper to taste*

In a bowl, empty the crab meat.
You can buy tubs of fresh crab meat ready prepared in some supermarkets.
Add the chopped radish and red onion.
Stir in the Hummus (see recipe) or Mayonnaise (see recipe) and mix thoroughly.
Put some spread thinly on the required amount of rice cakes.
Add a dollop of the crab mixture to the top of the rice cakes.
Garnish with chopped fresh chives.

# Roast Chicken
## with Lemon Gravy & Sesame Seed Parsnips

You can cook this recipe for Christmas lunch, if you serve it up with my Sage & Onion Stuffing Balls and other festive vegetables of your choice.

### Serves 4

*1 medium organic chicken (about 4lbs)*
*1 tablespoon of extra virgin olive oil*
*1 unwaxed, organic lemon*
*1 medium onion (peeled and left whole)*
*3 large cloves of garlic (unpeeled and whole)*
*3 large parsnips (cut into sticks)*
*1 - 2 tablespoons of extra virgin olive oil*
*2 level tablespoons of sesame seeds*
*1 - 2 dessert spoons of ground polenta*
*Sea salt and freshly ground black pepper to taste*

Preheat the oven to 180°C/350°F/gas mark 4.

Rinse the chicken with cold water, both inside and out (removing any giblets) then pat dry with kitchen towel.

In a large roasting tray, place the chicken right way up. Drizzle a little oil and salt and pepper over the skin.

Wash the lemon, prick it a couple of times with a knife then cut it in half. Place one lemon half inside.

Give this a squeeze inside the chicken cavity then add the onion, garlic cloves and other half of lemon.

Cook the chicken in the middle of the oven for 1 hour and 40 minutes. Baste with juices every 30 minutes.

(Note: Chicken is cooked for 20 minutes per pound, plus an extra 25 minutes of cooking time added).

Peel and chop the parsnips into sticks. In a pan of boiling water, parboil the parsnips for 2 - 3 minutes.

Pour the parsnips into a colander to drain the stock into a jug for use in the gravy later.

In a large bowl, add the parsnip sticks. Pour over the oil, sesame seeds and salt and pepper. Stir well.

In an ovenproof dish, lay the parsnips flat. Roast in the top of the oven 30 minutes from the end of cooking.

Cook for about 30 minutes until golden brown. Turn oven up to 180°C/350°F/gas mark 4, if slow to cook.

To make the gravy, drain off all the chicken juices into another roasting tray. Add ¼ pint of the stock to this.

Add the polenta flour spoon by spoon, stirring continuously to prevent lumps forming. Add more, if needed.

Remove the garlic from the chicken. Peel the cloves and add this to the gravy. Stir well until hot.

Pour the gravy into a gravy boat. Wait for it to settle then drain off excess oil with a spoon and discard it.

Serve with some fresh greens, sautéed in chopped garlic and onion, with a side dish of Chantenay carrots.

# Roasted Red Pepper
## and Garlic Pesto

This versatile recipe is perfect for basting meat or fish, or you can just serve it as a dip with some crudités. It can also be used as an alternative to mayonnaise or hummus, or used as a pasta sauce.

**Serves 3 - 4**

*2 large red peppers (cored, deseeded and halved)*
*2 large cloves of garlic (peeled and sliced)*
*1 - 2 tablespoons of extra virgin olive oil*
*1 heaped tablespoon of pine nuts*
*¼ teaspoon of dried thyme*
*1 teaspoon of fresh lemon juice*
*4 sun-dried tomatoes (rehydrated and chopped)*
*Pinch of sea salt and freshly ground black pepper*

Preheat the oven to 220°C/425°F/gas mark 7.

Slice the peppers in half and remove the stalk and seeds. Place skin side facing up on a roasting tray.

In the tray, add the garlic slices where there is a space. Drizzle a little oil over them.

Cook in the top of the oven for about 20 - 30 minutes until the pepper skins are blackened.

Remove from the oven and leave to cool for a few minutes before removing and discarding the skins.

Slice the peppers into chunks and add to a food processor, together with the roasted garlic and oil.

Add the pine nuts, thyme, lemon juice and chopped sun-dried tomatoes and a pinch of salt and pepper.

Blend the ingredients for a minute or so until it is a thick consistency. Add more oil if you think it needs it.

Now what are you going to do with it? There are just so many options!

# Roasted Romano Peppers
## with Quinoa Salad

This is another really tasty recipe, which is easy to make. You can always just eat the roasted peppers alone as an even quicker meal. Alternatively, roast them with onion, garlic, tomato and fresh basil.

### Serves 2 - 3

*2 large romano red peppers (halved)*
*1 - 2 tablespoons of extra virgin olive oil*
*1 large clove of garlic (peeled and sliced)*
*200g (7oz) of quinoa*
*1 yeast-free vegetable stock cube*
*1 handful of green beans (cut into 1 cm pieces)*
*¼ cucumber (cubed)*
*10 cherry tomatoes (quartered)*
*16 black olives (sliced)*
*5 radishes (trimmed and quartered)*
*1 x 150g tin of sweet corn*
*3 sun-dried tomatoes (soaked and chopped)*
*1 tablespoon of sunflower seeds*
*Sea salt and freshly ground black pepper to taste*

Preheat the oven to 190°C/375°F/gas mark 5.
Cut the peppers in half lengthways, or slit down one side to remain whole and remove the seeds.
Lay the peppers on an ovenproof dish, drizzle with oil and sprinkle over the garlic.
Place the dish on the middle shelf of the oven and bake for about 30 - 40 minutes.
In a jug, make up the stock cube with 1 pint of boiling water and pour in the pan.
Rinse the quinoa with cold water in a sieve.
In a wok, toast the quinoa by stirring for a minute or two before adding the stock. Mix well. Cover with a lid.
Simmer on a low heat for about 15 minutes, stirring often until all the water is absorbed.
(Note that the grain will turn from white to transparent and the spiral-like tail will appear when it is cooked).
When the quinoa is ready, stir in the salad vegetables.
Lay the peppers on a plate and spoon the quinoa over the peppers.
Serve straightaway whilst the peppers are still hot.

# Roasted Vegetable Quinoa

This recipe is one of my personal favourites. You can also add a tin of chick peas and serve with some fresh green beans.

### Serves 2 - 3
*2 small courgettes (trimmed and diced)*
*2 sticks of celery (trimmed and diced)*
*1 medium carrot (peeled and diced)*
*1 large red onion (peeled and diced)*
*4 large cloves of garlic (peeled and sliced roughly)*
*1 red pepper (cored, deseeded and diced)*
*2 tablespoons of rapeseed oil*
*1 teaspoon of fresh thyme (or dried)*
*1 yeast-free vegetable stock cube*
*200g (7oz) of quinoa*
*Sea salt and freshly ground black pepper to taste*

Preheat oven to 190°C/375°F/gas mark 5.
Chop up all the vegetables and garlic and lay them flat in a large ovenproof tray.
Sprinkle over the oil and add the thyme. Toss the vegetables in the oil.
Roast the vegetables in the oven for about 30 - 40 minutes. Cook for longer if needed.
In a jug, make up the stock cube with 1 pint of boiling water.
Rinse the quinoa with cold water in a sieve.
In a wok, toast the quinoa by stirring for a minute or two before adding the stock. Mix well.
Cover with a lid and simmer on a low heat for about 15 minutes, stirring often until all the water is absorbed.
(Note that the grain will turn from white to transparent and the spiral-like tail will appear when it is cooked).
When the quinoa is ready, add the roasted vegetables to the wok.
Stir thoroughly and warm through.

# Sage & Onion Stuffing Balls

Yes, you can have stuffing balls! Millet makes a great alternative to breadcrumbs when you can't have wheat. If you are vegan, replace the egg with a little dairy-free spread and maize flour to bind it.

**Serves 4 - 6**

*115g (4oz) of green millet (rinsed and cooked)*
*½ yeast-free vegetable stock cube*
*1 tablespoon of extra virgin olive oil*
*1 large clove of garlic (peeled and crushed)*
*1 large red onion (peeled and diced finely)*
*1 stick of celery (trimmed and diced finely)*
*2 tablespoons of freshly chopped sage*
*1 teaspoon of fresh lemon juice*
*1 medium organic egg*
*Pinch of sea salt and freshly ground black pepper*

In a sieve, rinse the millet with cold water and drain well.
In a wok or large pan with a lid, toast the millet on a low heat for 2 - 3 minutes, stirring continuously.
In a jug, make up the stock cube with 1½ pints of boiling water. Pour onto the millet and stir well.
Cover with a lid. Simmer on a low heat for 25 – 60 minutes (dependent on how refined your millet is).
Stir often until all the water is absorbed, or millet is cooked. Drain into a colander if there is excess water.
If the millet looks stodgy, you might want to rinse it over with a little boiling water. Leave it to drain.
Preheat the oven to 220°C/425°F/gas mark 7.
Add the chopped sage leaves to a small bowl of boiling water for 2 - 3 minutes to take away their raw edge.
Drain the sage water and save it to add to some vegetable stock for the freezer.
In a large pan, heat the oil on a medium heat. Fry the garlic, onion and celery until soft (about 5 minutes).
In a large mixing bowl, add the millet, cooked vegetables, sage and lemon juice. Break the egg into the dish.
Mix the ingredients together thoroughly with a spoon. Add a pinch of salt and pepper.
Scoop out a small amount of mixture to roll into a round stuffing ball with your hands to the required size.
Place the balls onto a tray and bake in the top of the oven for 25 - 30 minutes until they start to go crispy.

# Salmon & Scrambled Egg

If you are a vegan this meal won't be of much use to you, so why not stir-fry 50g of fresh tofu instead. Marinate it in some Bragg Liquid Aminos and spices of your choice.

**Serves 1**

*2 large organic eggs*
*1 large knob of dairy and gluten-free spread*
*1 tablespoon of organic, unsweetened soya milk*
*1 small meaty salmon fillet (sliced finely)*
*3 cherry tomatoes (sliced)*
*Freshly chopped chives to garnish*
*Sea salt and freshly ground black pepper to taste*

Break the eggs into a bowl and whisk. Stir in the soya milk.

In a small frying pan, add the spread. Wait for this to melt then add the salmon.

Scramble on a medium heat for about 5 minutes until cooked through. Push to one side of the pan.

Add the eggs and scramble until cooked, bringing the salmon in to warm through at the end.

If you want to avoid frying, you can bake the salmon in foil in the oven and soft boil the egg.

Sprinkle with chives and eat immediately.

Alternatively, serve with some green beans or salad and have it as a quick and easy evening meal.

You can also halve the amounts for this dish and have it as a breakfast.

# Salmon Fishcakes
## with Salsa Dip

If you have a toddler, this is a great recipe for a Saturday morning. They can be up to their elbows in mash helping you make their lunch!

**Serves 2 - 3**

1 meaty salmon fillet (skinned and boneless)
1 small knob of dairy and gluten-free spread
3 medium baking potatoes (peeled and quartered)
1 tablespoon of organic, unsweetened soya milk
3 spring onions (trimmed and chopped)
1 heaped tablespoon of freshly chopped parsley or dill
50g (1¾oz) of sesame seeds
2 tablespoons of extra virgin olive oil
Sea salt and freshly ground black pepper to taste
Salsa Dip (see recipe)

Place the salmon in a foil parcel in the oven, adding a small knob of spread to the top of the fillet.
Bake in the oven at 190°C/375°F/gas mark 5 for about 20 - 25 minutes. Check it is cooked.
Peel the potatoes and cook in a pan of boiling water for about 20 minutes.
When they are cooked, add a knob of spread and the soya milk and mash until a creamy consistency.
Transfer the mash to a large mixing bowl and mix in the spring onion and herb of your choice.
Flake the salmon and add this to the mixture. Leave to cool slightly.
Pour enough sesame seeds onto a large plate to cover it.
Spoon up a handful of mash and roll it into a ball the size of a small tennis ball.
Squash it flat into a muffin shape and place it on the plate of sesame seeds to cover both sides.
Pour 2 tablespoons of oil in a frying pan and when hot place the fishcakes in for a couple of minutes.
Keep turning them until they are warmed through and the sesame seeds are toasted. Do not burn.
They don't necessarily keep their circular shape, but you can mould them back.
Do as many of these as you want to eat. This amount of mixture makes about 5 decent sized fishcakes.
However, you can make a larger batch and wrap each fishcake individually in cling film and freeze them.
Serve the fishcakes warm with Salsa Dip (see recipe).

# Salsa Dip

You can always use this delicious dip as a replacement for when you would have normally used tomato ketchup on your food. However, always check your tomato purée does not contain citric acid.

**Serves 2 - 3**

*4 fresh medium tomatoes (peeled, cored and chopped)*
*1 small clove of garlic (peeled and chopped finely)*
*¼ small red onion (peeled and chopped)*
*1 level tablespoon of freshly chopped coriander*
*3 teaspoons of tomato purée*
*1 teaspoon of fresh lemon juice*
*Small pinch of cayenne pepper (optional)*
*Sea salt or freshly ground black pepper to taste*

Place the tomatoes in a large bowl of boiling water for 5 - 10 minutes until the skin becomes loose.
Remove from the water.
Peel the tomato skin, discard, remove the core and then chop the tomatoes into small or chunky pieces.
Add the chopped tomatoes to another bowl.
Finely chop the garlic and onion. Mix in with the tomatoes.
Add the coriander, tomato purée and lemon juice. Stir thoroughly.
Put in a pinch of the spices, to your own taste.
Cover the bowl with cling film and place it in the fridge.
Eat the dip within 24 hours.

# Seaweed & Spicy Chick Pea Soup

You could always add some cubes of cooked chicken to this dish to make it a more substantial meal. Remember, if you are going to use dried chick peas you will need to allow time to prepare them.

### Serves 3 - 4

*2 tablespoons of extra virgin olive oil*
*2 teaspoons of turmeric*
*3 teaspoons of ground cumin*
*¼ teaspoon of cayenne pepper (optional)*
*1 large onion (peeled and chopped)*
*2 x 400g tins of chick peas (or 200g dried)*
*2 - 3 sheets of seaweed (Japanese Kombu)*
*1 yeast-free vegetable stock cube*
*1 tablespoon of fresh lemon juice*
*Sea salt and freshly ground black pepper to taste*

If using tinned chick peas, drain them in a colander and rinse thoroughly with cold water and set aside.
If you are going to use dried peas, you will need less in weight as they expand in size as they rehydrate.
You will need to prepare 100g of dried peas per 400g tinned peas and soak them for the required time.
Follow the relevant instructions for cooking the chick peas from dried. Tinned are so easy!
In a small bowl, mix the turmeric, cumin, cayenne pepper and a small pinch of sea salt.
In a large pan, soak the seaweed in 2 pints of water for about 20 - 30 minutes.
Then bring it slowly to the boil and gently simmer for 5 minutes.
Remove the kombu from the pan, chop it into pieces and set it aside for later.
In a separate pan, heat the oil and add the spices.
Put in the onion and fry on a medium heat for about 5 minutes until soft. Stir regularly.
Transfer the onion to the kombu stock in the large pan.
In a jug, make up the stock cube with enough boiling water to break it down and pour this in with the onion.
You can always use some homemade chicken stock, if you would prefer.
Add the cooked chick peas to the large pan. Mix in thoroughly.
Simmer gently for 30 - 45 minutes until the liquid has much reduced, stirring regularly.
Return the seaweed to the pan then stir in the lemon juice. Serve hot.

# Shepherd's Pie

You cannot beat a home cooked shepherd's pie. There won't be any pie left over when you serve this up at the dinner table! A really hearty meal.

### Serves 3 - 4

*8 medium potatoes (peeled and quartered)*
*Small pinch of sea salt*
*400g (14oz) of organic lamb mince*
*1 large onion (peeled and chopped)*
*2 medium carrots (peeled and diced)*
*115g (4oz) of petit pois*
*2 teaspoons of freshly chopped rosemary*
*Gluten-free vegetable gravy mix*
*1 large knob of dairy and gluten-free spread*
*Sea salt and freshly ground black pepper to taste*

Cook the potatoes in a pan of boiling water on a medium heat for about 20 minutes until just cooked.
In a wok or large frying pan, stir-fry the lamb mince without any oil.
When almost cooked, add the onion, carrot, peas and rosemary
Fry on a medium heat for about 5 minutes until the vegetables soften. Remove any excess oil.
In a measuring jug, add 400ml of boiling water.
Stir in the gravy mix 1 teaspoon at a time, as per the amount required on the pack instructions.
Add more gravy powder if you like your gravy thick.
Add the gravy to the mince and vegetables then pour the mixture into a shallow ovenproof dish.
Preheat the oven to 180°C/350°F/gas mark 4.
Drain the cooked potatoes and mash with a knob of spread until a thick, creamy consistency.
Spoon the mashed potato on top of the lamb mixture making sure it doesn't leak over the side.
Flatten the mash potato down gently then run a fork over it to give it a textured appearance.
Bake it in the oven for about 20 minutes, or until heated through.
Serve with vegetables of your choice.

# Spaghetti Bolognese

Here's another family favourite, which I have adapted for our use. We may not be able to smother it with parmesan cheese, but there is a great dairy-free Parmazano alternative out there. Bon appétit!

## Serves 4

*1 tablespoon of extra virgin olive oil*
*4 large cloves of garlic (peeled and chopped)*
*1 teaspoon of freshly chopped oregano (or dried)*
*250g (8.8oz) organic beef (or lamb) mince*
*2 medium onions (peeled and chopped)*
*4 x 400g tins of tomatoes (or 16 fresh peeled tomatoes)*
*2 large carrots (peeled and cubed)*
*1 yeast-free vegetable stock cube*
*3 tablespoons of tomato purée*
*3 tablespoons of freshly chopped basil*
*200g (7oz) of corn spaghetti*
*Sea salt and freshly ground black pepper to taste*

In a large saucepan, heat the oil.
Add half of the garlic at this stage, together with a pinch of black pepper and the oregano.
Add the mince and cook until brown, stirring regularly. Remove the mince from the pan.
Cook the onion in the mince fat on a medium heat for about 5 minutes until soft. Drain off any excess oil.
Return the mince to the pan then add the carrot, tomatoes and tomato purée.
In a jug, make up the stock cube with 1 pint of boiling water.
Add half of the stock at this stage and keep adding more until it is the right consistency.
You don't want to add it all at once only to find the sauce is too runny.
Stir thoroughly. Cook on a low to medium heat for 30 - 45 minutes, stirring regularly.
Add the basil and remaining garlic and cook for a further 5 - 10 minutes. Leave to stand.
Cook the spaghetti pasta as per the pack instructions of whichever brand you are using.
Serve with a salad and some dairy-free Parmazano sprinkled on top.

# Spicy Butternut Squash Soup

Apart from this being a delicious soup, butternut squash contains a good number of healthy properties, so get it down you!

**Serves 4 - 6**

*1 large knob of dairy and gluten-free spread*
*1 small clove of garlic (peeled and crushed)*
*1 large onion (peeled and chopped)*
*1 large leek (trimmed and sliced)*
*1 teaspoon of cumin seeds*
*1 teaspoon of ground turmeric*
*1 teaspoon of fresh ginger (peeled and chopped)*
*1 teaspoon of ground coriander*
*1 medium butternut squash (peeled, deseeded and cubed)*
*1 large parsnip (peeled and cubed)*
*2 small potatoes (peeled and cubed)*
*1 yeast-free vegetable stock cube*
*½ pint of organic, unsweetened soya milk*
*Sea salt and freshly ground black pepper to taste*

Heat the spread in a large pan with a lid.
Add the garlic, onion, leek, cumin seeds, turmeric, ginger and coriander.
Stir on a medium heat for about 5 minutes until the onion softens.
Add the butternut squash, parsnip and potato.
In a jug, make up the stock cube with 2 pints of boiling water.
Stir well and then add the vegetable stock to the pan.
Cover and simmer for 30 minutes or until the vegetables are cooked, stirring regularly.
Add the soya milk, warming through gently (if overheated the soya milk goes frothy).
Blend with a hand-held blender.

# Spicy Lentil Soup

Lentils are full of B vitamins, but are also rich in protein, fibre and certain minerals which help support the strength of the immune system. We could all do with some help with that!

**Serves 4**

*1 tablespoon of extra virgin olive oil*
*2 teaspoons of ground cumin*
*2 teaspoons of ground coriander*
*1 large clove of garlic (peeled and crushed)*
*1 large onion (peeled and chopped)*
*2 small carrots (peeled and cubed)*
*2 sticks of celery (trimmed and sliced)*
*1½ pints of vegetable stock*
*140g (5oz) of red or green lentils (or a mix of both)*
*1 heaped tablespoon of tomato purée*
*Fresh coriander to garnish*
*Sea salt and freshly ground black pepper to taste*

In a large cooking pot with a lid, heat the oil and add the spices. Stir the oil.
Add the garlic, onion and fry gently on a medium heat for about 5 minutes until it softens.
Add the carrot and celery and stir for a minute or so.
Add the stock, lentils and tomato purée. Stir well.
(Note that green lentils do take longer to cook than red ones, so you might want to soak them overnight).
Cover and simmer on a low heat for about 45 minutes, or until the lentils are cooked to your taste.
Serve as it is if you like your soup with texture, or liquidise with a hand-held blender, if you prefer it smooth.
Serve in a bowl and garnish with fresh coriander.

# Spinach Soup

This is a great source of iron and tasty as well. To make this soup creamier, add ½ pint of organic, unsweetened soya milk, if you like.

**Serves 4**
*1 large knob of dairy and gluten-free spread*
*1 large clove of garlic (peeled and crushed)*
*1 large leek (trimmed and sliced)*
*2 medium onions (peeled and chopped)*
*1 small potato (peeled and diced)*
*2 small carrots (peeled and diced)*
*1 medium parsnip (peeled and diced)*
*200g (7oz) of fresh spinach (sliced finely)*
*1 yeast-free vegetable stock cube*
*Freshly chopped chives*
*Sea salt and freshly ground black pepper to taste*

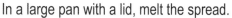

In a large pan with a lid, melt the spread.
Add the garlic, leek and onion and stir on a medium heat for about 5 minutes until they soften.
Add the potato, carrot, parsnip and spinach.
In a jug, make up the stock cube with 2 pints of boiling water.
Stir well and then add the vegetable stock.
Simmer for 30 minutes or until the vegetables are cooked, stirring regularly.
Blend with hand-held blender when cooled slightly.
Serve in a bowl and sprinkle chives over the soup to garnish.

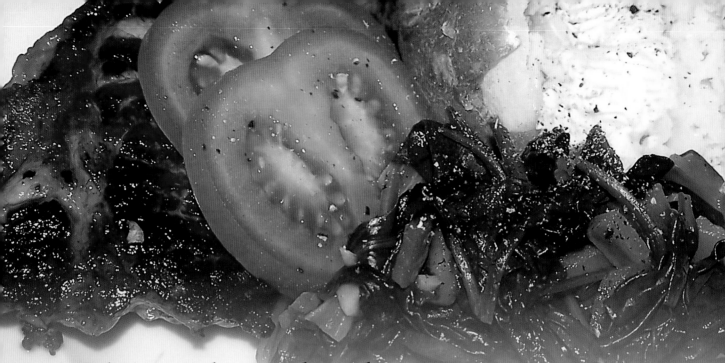

# Steak with Baked Potato
## & Wilted Baby Spinach

If you need to boost your iron levels then what better way to do it … this meal idea is much tastier than popping a pill! Have this as a treat when you need to increase your energy.

### Serves 2

*2 small baking potatoes (Maris Piper or King Edward)*
*2 small organic beef steaks (sirloin, rump, fillet or rib-eye)*
*4 cloves of garlic (peeled and chopped roughly)*
*1 - 2 tablespoons of extra virgin olive oil*
*1 small red onion (peeled and chopped)*
*200g of fresh baby spinach (washed)*
*¼ teaspoon of fresh nutmeg (grated)*
*1 knob of dairy and gluten-free spread*
*Sea salt and freshly ground black pepper to taste*

Preheat the oven to 200°C/400°F/gas mark 6. Scrub the potatoes and prick them with a fork a few times.
Bake in the oven for 30 minutes to 1 hour, depending on size/type of potato, until cooked and skins are crisp.
Tenderise the steak by laying it on a chopping board and pounding it all over with a meat mallet or rolling pin.
Pound the steak for about a minute then rub one side with 2 cloves of garlic and black pepper.
About 10 minutes before your potato is ready, preheat a griddle/frying pan on a high heat for 1 - 2 minutes.
You do not need to add any oil to a griddle pan, just make sure it's nice and hot. Or you can add some oil.
The cooking time depends on the cut of meat - e.g. if a ¾" sirloin, rump or rib eye steak, cook as follows:
Rare: 2½ minutes per side; medium 4 minutes per side or well done 6 minutes per side.
Thicker steaks will need an extra 1 - 2 minutes each side. It is all down to personal taste.
Add the steaks to the pan. You only need to turn the steaks once during cooking, so they remain succulent.
In a separate frying pan or wok, heat 1 - 2 tablespoons of oil on a low heat.
Add the remaining 2 cloves of chopped garlic and onion and cook for about 5 minutes until soft.
Put in the spinach and nutmeg and stir for a couple of minutes until the spinach begins to wilt.
When the steak and spinach are done, turn off the heat.
Prepare your baked potato by cutting it open, mashing the inside and adding a dollop of spread to the top.
Dish up everything onto a plate and serve with a big bowl of colourful salad.

# Stir-Fried Tofu
## with Chop Suey & Rice

This is a great recipe to impress your vegan and vegetarian friends with. It is a tasty, healthy and simple dish, which you can make look really impressive with some fancy Chinese crockery.

**Serves 4**

225g (8oz) of brown basmati and wild rice
200g (7oz) of fresh tofu (chopped into bite-sized pieces)
2 teaspoons of Bragg Liquid Aminos
2 tablespoons of rapeseed oil
2 large cloves of garlic (peeled and chopped)
3 heaped teaspoons of freshly chopped root ginger
1 small red onion (peeled and sliced)
1 red or yellow pepper (cored, deseeded and cut into rings)
3 pak choi (trimmed and chopped)
175g of fresh bean sprouts
100g (3½oz) each of fresh baby corn and mange tout
3 tablespoons of Bragg Liquid Aminos
Freshly ground black pepper to taste

In a large pan which has a lid, pour in about 1½ pints of boiling water and a small drop of oil.
In a sieve, add the rice and rinse well with cold water then add the rice to the pan.
Cover and simmer on a low heat, stirring occasionally, for about 25 - 30 minutes until cooked.
In a colander, drain the cooked rice then rinse well with boiling water until the water runs clear. Set aside.
Prepare the tofu by draining off the excess water and then cutting it into bite-sized cubes or strips.
Put the tofu pieces into a bowl and mix in 2 teaspoons of Bragg Liquid Aminos. Stir well.
In a frying pan, stir-fry the tofu in a little oil for about 10 minutes until brown and crispy on the outside.
In a wok, heat the oil on a medium heat and stir-fry the garlic, ginger and onion for about 2 - 3 minutes.
Put in the pepper and pak choi and cook for a further 2 minutes.
Add the bean sprouts and 3 tablespoons of Bragg Liquid Aminos. Stir-fry for 2 more minutes. Turn off the heat.
In a steamer, steam the baby corn and mange tout for about 2 - 3 minutes, so they have bite to them.
Put some of the rice in a small cup and press it down until it reaches the top.
Then put your serving plate over the top and tip them both upside down, so the rice is a little mound.
Serve with the chop suey and side vegetables and then sprinkle the tofu pieces over the top.

# Stuffed Marrow

Not many people know what to do with a marrow, other than use it as a potential murder weapon. Well this is a great recipe for you to get rid of the evidence!

### Serves 2 - 3

*1 marrow (approx 10 inches long)*
*1 teaspoon of turmeric*
*225g (8oz) of brown basmati rice*
*1 tablespoon of extra virgin olive oil*
*2 large cloves of garlic (peeled and chopped)*
*1 large red onion (peeled and cubed)*
*1 orange pepper (cored, deseeded and cubed)*
*10 sun-dried tomatoes (soaked and chopped)*
*20 black olives (sliced)*
*2 tablespoons of freshly chopped basil*
*Sea salt and freshly ground black pepper to taste*

Preheat the oven to 190°C/375°F/gas mark 5.
In a large pan with a lid, pour in 1½ pints of boiling water, a small drop of oil and the turmeric.
In a sieve, add the rice and rinse well with cold water then put the rice in the pan.
Cover and simmer on a low heat, stirring occasionally, for about 25 - 30 minutes until cooked.
In a colander, drain the cooked rice then rinse well with boiling water until the water runs clear. Set aside.
Slice the marrow in half lengthways and remove the seeds and core to create a hollow.
Place the two marrow halves hollow side facing up in a roasting tray and drizzle with oil.
Cover the tray with foil and bake in the oven for about 45 minutes, checking and basting it regularly with the oil.
In a large wok or pan, add the oil and stir-fry the garlic, onion and pepper on a medium heat until they soften.
Add the cooked rice to the pan of vegetables, together with the sun-dried tomatoes, olives and basil.
When you are happy that the marrow is almost cooked, spoon some of the rice stuffing in.
Cover the roasting tray with foil again and bake for a further 15 - 30 minutes, depending on the marrow.
Take the foil off about 5 minutes before it is ready to crisp the top of the rice.
Serve with some salad vegetables.

# Sunday Lamb Roast

Put the vegetables in some serving bowls with lids on to keep warm in the oven, then load up the kitchen table with all the food and have yourself a veritable feast with friends or family. Roll on Sunday!

### Serves 4

*1 large leek (trimmed and sliced chunkily)*
*1 x 900g organic lamb joint (leg or shoulder)*
*2 large cloves of garlic (peeled and chopped roughly)*
*3 tablespoons of fresh rosemary (keep needles whole)*
*Small pinch of sea salt and freshly ground black pepper*
*500g (17½ oz) of organic King Edward potatoes*
*3 medium carrots (peeled and sliced diagonally)*
*Green beans (trimmed and chopped in half)*
*½ medium swede (peeled and grated finely)*
*Gluten-free vegetable gravy mix*

Preheat the oven to 180°C/350°F/gas mark 4. Lay the leeks in the bottom of the roasting tin.
Rinse the lamb joint with cold water and then pat dry with kitchen towel. Place the lamb on top of the leeks.
Sprinkle over the garlic, half of the rosemary, a pinch of sea salt and black pepper. Drizzle over a little oil.
Cook the lamb in the middle of the oven for 1½ hours (depending on the size of the joint).
Lamb is best cooked at about 30 minutes per 450g/1lb, plus an extra 30 minutes, if you like it well done.
Baste the lamb with the juices 2 - 3 times throughout the cooking time.
Prepare the Crispy Herbed Potatoes (see recipe) using the rosemary left over.
About 15 minutes before the end, add the carrots to the boiling water in the bottom of a steamer.
Then 5 minutes later add the green beans to a steamer tray and cook for a further 5 minutes.
Add the swede to the top steamer tray to cook for about 5 minutes at the end. Save the stock for the gravy.
When the lamb is cooked, take it out of the oven. Place the lamb and the leeks on a carving board to rest.
Drain off the meat juices (keep some in reserve to add to the gravy as a naughty treat, if you want).
Make the gravy with the stock, as per the pack instructions, depending on what quantity you are making.
Pour the gravy into the roasting tin and warm through, adding more gravy powder and meat juices to thicken.
Enjoy!

# Tabbouleh

This is a variation on a theme of the Middle Eastern salad which traditionally uses bulgar wheat. I think quinoa works just as well and you won't have a bloated stomach afterwards ... unless you over-eat!

### Serves 3 - 4

200g (7oz) of quinoa
1 yeast-free vegetable stock cube
15 cherry tomatoes (chopped)
½ cucumber (chopped)
3 - 4 spring onions (trimmed and chopped)
2 tablespoons of extra virgin olive oil
3 tablespoons of fresh lemon juice
1 small clove of garlic (peeled and chopped finely)
½ teaspoon of ground cumin
½ teaspoon of ground cinnamon
2 tablespoons of freshly chopped mint
3 tablespoons of freshly chopped parsley
Sea salt and freshly ground black pepper to taste

In a sieve, rinse the quinoa with cold water and drain.
In a wok, toast the quinoa on a low heat for a minute.
In a jug, make up the stock cube with 1 pint of boiling water. Add the stock to the quinoa and stir well.
Cover with a lid and simmer on a low heat for about 15 minutes until all the water is absorbed. Stir regularly.
(Note that the grain will turn from white to transparent and the spiral-like tail will appear when it is cooked).
When it is ready, transfer it to a large salad bowl to cool.
Chop the tomatoes and cucumber into bite-sized chunks. Thinly slice the spring onions.
Finely chop the parsley and mint.
In a measuring jug, mix the oil, lemon juice, garlic and spices for the dressing. Add a little more oil if needed.
Add the vegetables and herbs to the quinoa. Stir thoroughly.
Pour over the salad dressing (you do not have to use all the dressing if you do not want to).
Refrigerate for 30 minutes for the flavours to infuse.
Eat on its own, or serve as a side salad to some meat or fish.

# Thai Noodle Soup

This soup would usually involve chilli, but just add cayenne pepper to it instead, if you can tolerate it. For you meat eaters, it is also tastier if you can use chicken stock instead of vegetable stock.

### Serves 2

*1 tablespoon of extra virgin olive oil*
*2 large cloves of garlic (peeled and crushed)*
*2 teaspoons of freshly chopped ginger*
*1 yeast-free vegetable stock cube*
*Small pinch of cayenne pepper (optional)*
*1 x 400ml tin of coconut milk*
*2 x pak choi (trimmed and sliced)*
*1 tablespoon of freshly chopped basil*
*85g (3oz) of organic brown rice and wakame noodles*
*Sea salt and freshly ground black pepper to taste*

In a wok, heat the oil and stir-fry the garlic and ginger on a medium heat for a couple of minutes.
In a jug, make up the stock cube with about ¾ pint of boiling water.
Add the stock, pinch of cayenne pepper and coconut milk to the pan.
Bring to the boil and cook for about 5 minutes.
Trim off the root end of the stalk of the pak choi and discard this.
Slice up the rest of the pak choi, including the stems and the leaves.  Add to the wok.
Simmer for about another 5 minutes.
In a large pan of boiling water, cook the noodles as per the pack instructions.
When the noodles are cooked, divide them into two soup bowls.
You can mix the noodles by using black rice noodles for half of the amount to make it look more interesting.
Ladle a couple of spoonfuls of the soup over the noodles until they are covered.
Sprinkle with basil and serve immediately.

# Trout
## with Avocado & Tomato Salad

You've probably never considered putting trout with avocado before, but you will be surprised by how much the flavours really complement each other.  Give it a go!

### Serves 2

*2 large trout fillets (deboned)*
*1 - 2 tablespoons of extra virgin olive oil*
*2 tablespoons of freshly chopped coriander*
*2 tablespoons of freshly chopped basil*
*2 tablespoons of freshly chopped parsley*
*1 large ripe avocado (peeled, de-stoned and sliced)*
*I large fresh beef tomato (sliced and cored)*
*1 small red onion (peeled and sliced)*
*5 fresh basil leaves*
*1 teaspoon of extra virgin olive oil*
*½ tablespoon of fresh lemon juice*
*1 tablespoon of pumpkin seeds*
*Sea salt and freshly ground black pepper to taste*

Wash and debone the trout.  Baste the fillet on both sides with oil.
Chop the coriander, basil and parsley (leaving 5 fresh basil leaves aside for the salad).
Put the chopped herbs in a small bowl and stir in 1 tablespoon of oil and 1 tablespoon of lemon juice.
Heat a griddle pan on a medium heat and place the oiled trout in the pan skin side down.
Cook for about 3 - 5 minutes (depending on how thick the fillet is).
Spread the herb mixture over the top of the fillet then turn it over so it is flesh side down.
Cook for a further 3 - 5 minutes, or until you are happy with the way it is cooked.
Place the trout fillet on a plate.
Serve with Avocado & Tomato Salad (see recipe).

# Tuna & Kidney Bean Salad

You don't have to just restrict yourself to tuna in this recipe. You can add some cooked chicken breast or even some marinated tofu instead.

**Serves 3 - 4**

*1 handful of fresh green beans*
*1 x 400g tin of kidney beans (or 100g dried)*
*120g of mixed salad leaves*
*8 cherry tomatoes (halved)*
*¼ cucumber (sliced and quartered)*
*½ yellow pepper (cored, deseeded and sliced)*
*1 x 185g tin of tuna in sunflower oil, brine or spring water*
*¼ small red onion (peeled and chopped finely)*
*Hummus*
*14 black olives (leave whole)*
*1 tablespoon of pumpkin seeds*
*1 tablespoon of avocado oil*
*Sea salt and freshly ground black pepper to taste*

If using tinned beans, drain them in a colander and rinse thoroughly with cold water and set aside.
If you are going to use dried beans, you will need less in weight as they expand in size as they rehydrate.
You will need to prepare 100g of dried beans per 400g tinned beans and soak them for the required time.
Follow the relevant instructions for cooking the particular types of beans from dried. Tinned are so easy!
In a small pan of boiling water, cook the green beans for about 5 - 10 minutes, or until just tender.
In a large salad bowl, place the mixed leaves. Shred some of the larger lettuce pieces.
Arrange the tomato, cucumber, pepper, kidney beans and green beans on top of the lettuce.
Drain the can of tuna and add to a smaller mixing bowl.
Add the onion and a dollop of Hummus (see recipe) to the tuna and mix thoroughly.
Serve some of the salad onto a plate. Add the tuna mixture to the centre.
Sprinkle over the olives and some pumpkin seeds.
Drizzle with a little avocado oil.

# Tuscan Bean Soup

I never tire of soup, as it makes such an easy and filling lunch. You can use any beans you fancy in this recipe. Why not try adzuki or flageolet beans, or some exotic legume you've never tried before?

**Serves 4**

2 tablespoons of extra virgin olive oil
1 large onion (peeled and chopped)
2 large cloves of garlic (peeled and chopped)
3 sticks of celery (trimmed and sliced)
1 small carrot (peeled and sliced)
2 x 400g tins of tomatoes (or 8 fresh peeled tomatoes)
1 yeast-free vegetable stock cube
3 fresh bay leaves
1 x 400g tin of borlotti beans (or 100g dried)
1 x 400g tin of butter beans (or 100g dried)
50g of fresh spinach, Swiss chard or kale (sliced)
1 tablespoon each of freshly chopped thyme and rosemary.
1 tablespoon of tomato purée
Sea salt and freshly ground black pepper to taste

If using tinned beans, drain them in a colander and rinse thoroughly with cold water and set aside.
If you are going to use dried beans, you will need less in weight as they expand in size as they rehydrate.
You will need to prepare 100g of dried beans per 400g tinned beans and soak them for the required time.
Follow the relevant instructions for cooking the particular types of beans from dried. Tinned are so easy!
In a large pan with a lid, heat the oil.
Add the onions and garlic and cook on a medium heat for about 5 minutes until soft, stirring regularly.
In a jug, make up the stock cube with 1½ pints of boiling water.
Stir in the celery, carrot, tomatoes, stock and bay leaves.
Bring to the boil and then simmer for about 20 minutes. Stir occasionally.
Mix in the cooked beans, spinach and herbs. Simmer for a further 15 minutes.
Add the tomato purée. You can always add more than 1 tablespoon if the soup needs thickening.
Serve immediately or stock a few tubs in your freezer for lunches in the week.

# Vegetable & Olive Pasta

This is a very simple vegetarian recipe, but if you are a meat or fish eater, you can always add some cooked king prawns or chicken to this dish for some extra protein.

### Serves 2 - 3

*250g (8.8oz) of vegetable rice pasta*
*2 tablespoons of extra virgin olive oil*
*2 large cloves of garlic (peeled and chopped)*
*1 large red onion (peeled and chopped)*
*1 large courgette (trimmed, sliced and halved)*
*1 tablespoon of freshly chopped rosemary*
*25 black olives (whole)*
*16 cherry tomatoes (halved)*
*Sea salt and freshly ground black pepper to taste*

In a very large pan, add about 4 litres (135 fl oz) of boiling water for every 250g (8.8oz) of pasta.

Stir gently and simmer on a medium heat for about 8 - 10 minutes until cooked.

Drain the pasta into a colander and rinse well with boiling water.

In a wok, heat up the oil.  Add the garlic, onion, courgette and rosemary.

Cook on a medium heat for about 10 minutes.

When done, add the pasta and olives.  Add a little more olive oil, if required.

Put in the tomatoes at the very end just to warm them through.  Do not overcook as their skins will become wrinkly.

Serve alone or with a side salad and a sprinkling of dairy-free Parmazano.

# Vegetable Omelette

This is a quick, easy and filling meal for when you don't have a lot of time or energy to cook after a hard day at work. It's always a firm favourite too.

### Serves 4

2 tablespoons of sunflower oil
1 large clove of garlic (peeled and chopped)
1 medium red onion (peeled and sliced in rings)
1 small courgette (trimmed and chopped in sticks)
1 red pepper (cored, deseeded and sliced)
20 black olives (whole)
6 sun-dried tomatoes (soaked and chopped)
5 large organic eggs
1 tablespoon of organic, unsweetened soya milk
1 tablespoon of freshly chopped parsley
Sea salt and freshly ground black pepper to taste

In a large round frying pan, heat the oil. Add the garlic, onion, courgette and red pepper.
Fry for about 10 minutes until the vegetables have softened, but still have a slight crunch to them.
Add the olives and sun-dried tomatoes to the pan.
Break the eggs into a mixing bowl and add the soya milk. Whisk thoroughly.
Add the parsley and a pinch of sea salt and black pepper to the egg mixture. Stir in.
Pour the egg into the pan onto the vegetables and mix in quickly so all are covered evenly.
Cook on a low heat for about 5 - 10 minutes (check by poking a knife into the middle to see if it is still liquid).
Turn on the grill and heat the top of the omelette for about 5 minutes or until cooked. Do not burn!
Cover the pan with a large plate (top side facing down).
Turn the pan upside down so the omelette falls onto the plate.
Do this again with another plate so that the omelette is the right way up.
Serve with a salad or have some for breakfast.

# Vegetable Pilaf

My vegetarian friend, Tim, came round to validate this particular recipe. I like to feed him vegetables now and then otherwise he would just live on Bombay mix. He had two helpings, so there you go!

## Serves 4

*2 tablespoons of extra virgin olive oil*
*2 large cloves of garlic (peeled and chopped)*
*1 large onion (peeled and chopped)*
*1 small carrot (peeled and cubed)*
*1 stick of celery (trimmed and sliced)*
*1 medium courgette (trimmed and cubed)*
*1 x 400g tin of organic mixed beans (or 100g dried)*
*115g (4oz) of petit pois*
*225g (8oz) of brown basmati rice*
*1 yeast-free vegetable stock cube*
*½ teaspoon of ground turmeric*
*1 heaped tablespoon each of freshly chopped coriander and mint*
*Sea salt and freshly ground black pepper to taste*

If using tinned beans, drain them in a colander and rinse thoroughly with cold water and set aside.

If you are going to use dried beans, you will need less in weight as they expand in size as they rehydrate. You will need to prepare 100g of dried beans per 400g tinned beans and soak them for the required time. Follow the relevant instructions for cooking the particular types of beans from dried. Tinned are so easy!

In a wok, heat the oil. Add the garlic (half of it), onion, carrot and celery.

Cook on a medium heat for about 10 minutes, stirring regularly.

Pour the rice into a sieve and rinse with cold water then add it to the wok. Stir until it is coated with oil.

In a jug, make up the stock cube with 1¼ pints of boiling water.

Pour in the stock and add the turmeric. Mix in well.

Bring to the boil then simmer for about 50 minutes with the lid on, stirring regularly. Do not burn.

Add the courgette and rest of the garlic. Cook for about 10 minutes then stir in the cooked beans and peas.

Simmer until the rice is cooked, adding more stock/water, if necessary.

Serve with a sprinkling of coriander and mint over the top and a mixed salad.

# Vegetarian Paella

Apart from this being a fantastic recipe, in Chinese medicine, arame seaweed is used to detoxify the body … bring it on!

**Serves 3 - 4**

*1 small aubergine (trimmed and sliced)*
*225g (8oz) of brown basmati rice*
*2 tablespoons of extra virgin olive oil*
*1 medium carrot (peeled and sliced)*
*1 red pepper (cored, deseeded and sliced)*
*1 heaped teaspoon of turmeric*
*1 x 225g tin of braised tofu*
*2 - 3 tablespoons of fresh lemon juice*
*2 tablespoons of Bragg Liquid Aminos*
*2 tablespoons of arame sea vegetable (soaked and drained)*
*85g (3oz) of petit pois and 30 whole black olives*
*2 tablespoons of freshly chopped parsley*
*Freshly ground black pepper to taste*

Prepare the aubergine by trimming both ends off and slicing it into 1cm thick slices.
Spread the slices out onto a large place and sprinkle liberally with a little sea salt on both sides.
Leave to sit for 20 minutes then wash off the salt well with cold water and pat dry with kitchen towel.
In a large pan with a lid, pour in 1½ pints of boiling water and a small drop of oil.
In a sieve, add the rice and rinse well with cold water then put the rice in the pan.
Cover and simmer on a low heat, stirring occasionally, for about 25 - 30 minutes until cooked.
In a colander, drain the cooked rice then rinse well with boiling water until the water runs clear.  Set aside.
In a wok or large frying pan with a lid, heat the oil.  Cut the aubergine into cubes.
Cook on a medium heat for about 5 minutes then add the carrot, red pepper and turmeric.
Cover with the lid and sauté the vegetables until tender (about 10 - 15 minutes) stirring regularly.
Drain the juices from the tin of braised tofu.
Soak the arame in a bowl of cool water for 10 - 15 minutes.  (Note that it will double in size).  Drain well.
Stir in the cooked rice, petit pois, lemon juice and Bragg Liquid Aminos.  Gently fold in the tofu and arame.
Warm through for a couple of minutes.  Garnish with olives and parsley.

# Veggie Cayenne

You can go all out and serve this with all the trimmings: guacamole, tortilla chips and salsa dip for a great night in with friends.

**Serves 4 - 6**

*225g (8oz) of green lentils*
*2 tablespoons of sunflower oil*
*1 large onion (peeled and chopped)*
*3 large cloves of garlic (peeled and crushed)*
*¼ teaspoon of cayenne pepper (optional)*
*1 heaped teaspoon of ground cumin*
*1 red pepper and 1 green pepper (cored, deseeded and chopped)*
*1 large carrot (peeled and chopped)*
*2 large courgettes (trimmed and chopped)*
*2 x 400g tins of tomatoes (or 8 fresh peeled tomatoes)*
*1 heaped tablespoon of tomato purée*
*1 yeast-free vegetable stock cube*
*1 x 400g tin each of kidney beans and butter beans (or 100g dried each)*
*Sea salt and freshly ground black pepper to taste*

If using tinned beans, drain them in a colander and rinse thoroughly with cold water and set aside.
If you are going to use dried beans, you will need less in weight as they expand in size as they rehydrate.
You will need to prepare 100g of dried beans per 400g tinned beans and soak them for the required time.
Follow the relevant instructions for cooking the particular types of beans from dried.  Tinned are so easy!
Place the green lentils in a large bowl with boiling water.  Leave to soak for 30 minutes then drain.
Heat the oil in a large saucepan.  Fry the onion with two-thirds of the garlic.
Add the cayenne pepper and cumin and cook on a medium heat for 5 minutes until the onion is soft.
Add the peppers, carrot, courgette and drained green lentils. Stir thoroughly.
In a jug, make up the stock cube with 1 pint of boiling water.  Pour in the tomatoes, tomato purée and stock.
Cover with a lid and simmer for about 1 hour until the lentils and vegetables are tender, stirring regularly.
Put in the cooked kidney beans, butter beans and remaining raw garlic.  Simmer for 5 more minutes.
Serve with cooked brown rice, a dollop of Hummus (see recipe) and a sprinkling of fresh coriander.

# Warm Chicken Salad
## with Pepper & Fennel

This dish can also be served cold and eaten on a picnic, or a day out. I actually ate mine at the cinema whilst watching "Furry Vengeance" (not my choice, I hasten to add)!

### Serves 2

*1 organic chicken breast*
*1 red pepper (cored, deseeded and sliced)*
*1 fennel bulb (trimmed and cut into sticks)*
*2 tablespoons of pine nuts (toasted without oil)*
*1 large handful of fresh basil (chopped)*
*1 tablespoon of extra virgin olive oil*
*Sea salt and freshly ground black pepper to taste*

In a steamer, put enough water in the bottom pan to cook for 15 - 20 minutes.
Place the chicken breast on a steamer tray and steam for about 15 minutes.
Quarter the pepper and remove the seeds.
Place the pepper pieces skin side up on foil on a grill pan and grill until blackened.
When the pepper has cooled sufficiently, remove and discard the skin and slice the pepper.
Prepare the fennel and cut it into sticks.
Add the fennel to a separate tray in the steamer on top of the chicken and steam for 5 minutes.
In a small frying pan on a low heat, dry toast the pine nuts (without oil) until just golden.
Slice the chicken into bite-sized pieces.
In a large salad bowl, add the chicken, pepper, fennel, basil, pine nuts and a drizzle of olive oil.
Toss thoroughly and serve immediately.

# Watercress & Potato Salad

If you are keeping your carbohydrate intake low, you might want to halve the amount of potatoes in this recipe and bulk it out with cucumber or another salad vegetable of your choice instead.

**Serves 4**

*1lb (16oz) of small new potatoes (quartered)*
*75g of fresh watercress*
*14 cherry tomatoes (halved)*
*2 tablespoons of pumpkin seeds*
*2 - 3 tablespoons of homemade Mayonnaise (see recipe)*
*Sea salt and freshly ground black pepper to taste*

Wash the potatoes (but leave the skins on) then quarter them.
Cook the potatoes in a pan of boiling water until they are only just tender.
Drain and leave to cool.
In a large bowl, toss together the potatoes and Mayonnaise (see recipe).
Add the tomatoes and mix for a short time.
Add the watercress last. Do not stir it in too much as it will become limp with the Mayonnaise.
Sprinkle over the pumpkin seeds and serve immediately.

# Watercress Soup

This particular soup is always a firm favourite in my household, because of its unique flavour. Watercress has also been used for generations for its healing properties and is a rich source of iron.

### Serves 3 - 4

*1 large knob of dairy and gluten-free spread*
*1 large onion (peeled and chopped)*
*1 medium leek (trimmed and sliced)*
*1 small carrot (peeled and diced)*
*2 sticks of celery (trimmed and sliced)*
*150g of fresh watercress*
*2 fresh bay leaves*
*1 yeast-free vegetable stock cube*
*½ pint of organic, unsweetened soya milk*
*Sea salt and freshly ground black pepper to taste*


In a large pan with a lid, heat the spread.  When melted, add the onion and leek.
Cook on a medium heat until they soften, stirring regularly.
Add the carrot and celery.  Stir well
In a jug, make up the stock cube with 1½ pints of boiling water.
Pour in the stock and add the bay leaves and the watercress.
Cover with the lid and simmer on a low heat for 30 minutes or until the vegetables are cooked.  Stir often.
Remove the bay leaves.
Add the soya milk, warming through gently (if overheated the soya milk goes frothy).
Blend with a hand-held blender.
Serve in a bowl with a sprig of watercress on top.

# CHAPTER 6

## CANDIDA: MY STORY

About five years ago, I was sat in your place being diagnosed as a "Yeasty". What did I do? I burst into tears. Obviously, I was relieved at finding out that I wasn't a total mentalist, but then the realisation hit me that life was about to change dramatically and I got a bit grumpy as my poor Nutritionist, Katherine, told me everything that I couldn't eat for the foreseeable future. She then recommended to me a regime of supplements and a Candida book that explained everything. I hurried out to get this, as it was going to be my 'Bible' for information and meal ideas, which it was. However, the only disappointment for me was that it did not have a single picture of the food to whet my appetite. This is what inspired me to write my own book. I want to give my fellow sufferers hope and to literally SHOW you what you CAN eat instead of telling you what you CAN'T ... and it is actually pretty yummy.

*Rebecca Richardson*

Initially, it was a hard struggle collating all the information and discovering the recipes that I could eat, as a lot of them contained gluten, which I was personally intolerant to (hence the gluten-free recipes here). Each of us is individual and therefore some of us will have trouble with certain specific foods. I couldn't believe it when Katherine told me that my body could not tolerate onion and garlic. It was no wonder that I was rushing to the toilet within twenty minutes of eating, as these were the most used ingredients in my meals! You often find that the foods that you are intolerant to are the ones your body craves the most. Luckily for me, after a couple of months on the diet, I was then able to introduce garlic and onion back into my diet. Having got the Candida under control, my body was again able to tolerate these foods.

This is where I tell you all about my sordid past, including details of my ailments and symptoms in all their gory glory – hence why I've put this chapter after the recipes, so as not to put you off your food! I'm not going to lie to you, you need to have a will of iron to cope with this diet, especially when you are up against temptation of some sugary form or another on a daily basis (at least you are if you work in my office!). I am sad to say that the majority of people who are able to stick to the rule book and not eat the slightest thing that they shouldn't are usually the ones who are so ill and at the end of their tether that it is the only thing that is going to keep them going. I have felt suicidal on many an occasion. I couldn't go on feeling like I did for much longer. I was in constant pain, it ruined my sex life, my social life and I was unable to go anywhere without planning ahead on where the nearest toilet was going to be so that I wouldn't wet myself. Hard to believe that this nasty little bit of yeast can have that much control over you, isn't it? It is time to take the control back and show it who is boss.

Thinking back to my childhood, I now recognise that I had certain symptoms which my lifestyle was beginning to contribute to even then. The fact that I practically lived on raw sugar helped the early Candida set up home. 10 pence back in 1975 could secure you a can of fizzy drink and a hell of a lot of the sweet delights available in that era (I cannot ever remember drinking a glass of water without squash in it). I ate this on a daily basis after school and, if my dear mother were still alive to 'dish the dirt on me', she would say that I was an extremely hyperactive child and that Saturday nights always ended with a pile of vomit!

My first introduction to antibiotics was at around the age of five or six, after a summer holiday in Ibiza, where I learned to swim. By the end of the week I had been jumping off the diving board into the deep end, filling my ear drums with water ready for the cabin pressure on the flight back. By the time I got home, I was screaming in agony from earache. The doctor came and prescribed me a drug (which shall remain nameless, as I don't want to be sued) which they later discovered was not to be given to children under the age of eight, as it damaged their teeth. Fantastic! Now the long-term plan for a mouthful of mercury was set in motion. To be precise, nine fillings, two crowns and six porcelain veneers (the latter of which took nine injections to numb me as my teeth were so sensitive).

Then there was the wee issue. I can remember incidents of painful urination after long soaks in bubble baths, or trips to the swimming pool in the days when you used to have to wade ankle deep through disinfectant before you even reached the chlorine! Wearing tight jeans also caused me irritation. I often wonder if a fractured coccyx sustained in a freak 'pogoing' accident did anything to damage me 'downstairs'! An Osteopath, who I saw as an adult, recommended internal manipulation as the bottom bone was bent under. However, as you can imagine, this wasn't something I was keen to pursue!

My digestion problems probably also began around the age of eight with the large swig of lightly diluted washing up liquid, whilst playing 'bubbles'. Preparing my orange squash (evil in itself) and my bubble mixture in exact matching cups was, with hindsight, perhaps foolish! I had a sore throat for about a week. I can only imagine what it did to my intestines!

About this age, I also started to suffer with migraines. The first one was the most terrifying experience. Everything suddenly became brighter, sharper visually and loud. My little finger on my left hand started to tingle like pins and needles and then spread down my arm. After about a ten minute period, the whole left side of my body was numb, including half my tongue and brain. I couldn't write properly and I would talk gibberish. After this had passed, the headache would come on and that would put me in bed in a darkened room for 24 hours. I can't remember how frequently they came over the next few years, but I couldn't put them down to anything in particular. The migraines stopped when I was sixteen. It was around this time that I started taking the contraceptive pill for about ten years, and then off and on after that. I finally stopped taking the pill in 2002, only to find that condoms caused me real irritation. Joy!

My first kidney infection arrived at the age of seventeen. After a weekend of hard core drinking and enjoying myself a little too much, I got home from work one night and suddenly had to rush to the loo. Within seconds, I was in agony. My urgent wee was a few drops of urine that seemed to have turned to acid. I stood up and immediately felt like I needed to go again. This continued for a while until I started passing blood. The doctor was called out and I was prescribed antibiotics. During the next couple of days, I developed thrush and haemorrhoids. I felt pretty bloody awful until it eventually cleared up. Little was I to know that I had been given my first warning. Unfortunately for me, I didn't take any notice.

The next two decades of my life were dedicated to a hedonistic lifestyle. Alcohol was consumed in large quantities and mixtures (today I believe it has the term "binge drinking") and pasta and bread were the main ingredients of most meals. The invention of 'alcopops' coincided with me taking up smoking and then the real trouble began.

A dream trip to Australia and New Zealand became one of the most painful times of my life. It was a year's holiday, which involved daily smoking and drinking. Whenever I drank sweet alcoholic drinks, my cheeks would literally burn bright red. My thrush and cystitis were at their highest ebb and various trips to the doctor resulted in more antibiotics, even though they couldn't tell me what was actually wrong with me. I also ended up drinking a lot of cranberry juice not realising that it was making the symptoms worse, due to all the natural sugar content. Whilst travelling in New Zealand, I once even had to get my friend to pull the car over just so that I could take a pee in front of everyone on the main road. If the humiliation wasn't enough, it also hurt like hell.

Upon my return from Australia in 2004, I was at my worst. A friend suggested that I should visit her Nutritionist to see if my problems could be put down to food intolerance and allergies. I have never looked back. Katherine was so sympathetic and she actually listened. She diagnosed Candida through kinesiology and put me on the strict Candida diet.

Overleaf I am going to list my various symptoms over the years, which I can now put down to Candida, just so that you can maybe relate some of them to what you are personally going through:

## Ears, Nose, Throat and Mouth:

In 1994, I was diagnosed with asthma and given a steroid inhaler. Soon after this I started suffering from tonsillitis. I also developed a constant sore throat (worse at night, so I stopped using my facial moisturiser and this appeared to help). I had an operation to remove one tonsil in 2001, because it was swollen and there was throat/jaw discomfort. I also had a bit of left ear pain like earache and mucus in the back of my nose and throat. At one stage I had a nasal drip which made the skin at the entrance to my nostrils itchy, red and sore, which could have been associated with hay fever.

## Digestion:

I started to get a pain in the side of my stomach, just underneath my ribs, which turned into a painful stitch under my collarbone when I breathed. I usually had an upset stomach after eating, which caused haemorrhoids and let's also not forget the flatulence!

## Gynaecological:

I suffered with vaginal soreness and itching internally and externally, especially at night in bed. I couldn't wait to get to sleep to get some relief from it all, but then had to get up four or five times a night to wee. It is exhausting waking up that many times in the night as it does nothing for your good mood the following day. My periods never gave me any problems usually, but then I began to suffer with PMS and cramps when I never had before. It goes without saying that my libido simply disappeared without a trace. I had major mood swings, especially around my period. I could turn from being normal to being in a rage within seconds.

## Headaches:

These were irregular, but didn't feel like the migraines I had as a child. They were more like a pressure headache with cramps and made me feel very nauseous. I felt spaced out, couldn't concentrate and had occasional dizzy spells. It would be as if my brain had just frozen and I couldn't think straight. I also had weakness/shakiness on my right hand side in my arm and leg.

## Interstitial Cystitis:

In 2004, I had an IV X-ray on my kidneys and bladder. It showed nothing wrong, but there was some kind of calcium lump which the Doctor said would not cause the symptoms. In 2005, I was diagnosed as having Interstitial Cystitis ("IC"). My symptoms were frequent urination, urgency with a burning sensation, my bladder feeling inflamed from over-use and often felt 'niggly' as if there was sherbet in it. As soon as I would finish my wee, it would feel like I needed to go again, but couldn't. Some days I would wee lots and others I would drink lots of water and wee a little, but it would be more painful. I would experience shooting pains/twinges in the urethra about five minutes after passing water lasting for about five to ten minutes. My urine was not especially dark in colour, as I drank a lot of water. However, after taking the herbal supplements prescribed by my Nutritionist, it did make my urine look like floor cleaner! The anterior wall (the wall on the other side of the bladder) of my vagina was always irritated after I had urinated. This was due to inappropriate absorption of toxic chemicals through the bladder wall. My wee still causes me problems, especially when I am off my Candida diet, but absolutely nowhere near to how I was five years ago. I can cope with my symptoms now and even control them to some degree with the help of this diet.

I also have an extremely heightened sense of smell. Strong odours, such as aftershave, perfume, gas, petrol/diesel fumes, cigarette smoke, chemicals (especially bleach and disinfectant) and damp/mould send me mad. I have stopped wearing perfume and now use only natural toiletry products, such as sanitary towels produced by Natracare and toxin and chemical-free soaps, shampoos, make-up, etc. which I purchase online. Thankfully, there are a number of web sites now that sell such products, such as: www.beautynaturals.co.uk, www.spiritofnature.co.uk and www.natracare.com.

I once read somewhere that women can eat up to six pounds of lipstick in their lifetime! You might also want to think about this when you're worrying about what you are eating! As always, do check the ingredients very carefully before you purchase anything, as some still do contain perfume, etc.

## Obsessive Compulsive Disorder (OCD):

Since a child I have suffered with mild OCD. OCD equals stress and with stress and anxiety come exacerbated symptoms of Candida. What a vicious circle, eh? There have been some links made between Candida and OCD, but it would be interesting to know how many other sufferers have this also. It always is more pronounced when I am worried or upset about something. I just go on a mad cleaning spree. It is exhausting, but at least I've always got a tidy house!

I frequently suffered with depression, panic attacks and paranoia. I took anti-depressants for three months, following a very bad choice of employment. I also used to experience heart palpitations which felt like a missed beat. It could be very frightening and sometimes I had to punch myself in the chest. It would happen after running or climbing lots of stairs and then other times I could be sitting watching television and it would just do it for no reason. This sometimes occurs when you have eaten a food that you are intolerant to, so if you also suffer with this, you might want to keep a record of what you have eaten before it happens.

## Random Stuff:

My glands always feel slightly enlarged, but I have always been told this is probably because I have "no meat" on me. I am always cold to the marrow and it has been suggested that it is probably because I am "skin and bone". My eyeballs are always dry, apparently "because I do not blink enough"! I use eye drops on a daily basis for this. My energy levels would be up and down. Some days I just couldn't do anything and had to go to bed when I got home from work and others I was like a whirling dervish. When you think of all of the above symptoms, you can see why Candida is closely linked to ME.

## Skin:

I had an itchy patch on the sole (curiously around the bladder/urethra area for reflexology!) and heel of my foot, palm of hand and armpit. You couldn't see them, but they itched like crazy.

The path to recovery is a process of elimination. I started taking note of my symptoms and keeping a record of what food I had eaten on the particular day that my aches and pains were most prominent. For example, I noticed that after eating curry, my vagina would sting and feel irritated and swollen, as opposed to itchy. From then on I replaced the chilli with a pinch of cayenne pepper and this seemed to help. Simply making certain changes, such as not wearing tights, knickers or trousers constantly (even going 'commando') made a difference to how it felt. On days that I didn't drink a large amount of water, I noticed my wee played up. I also started to treat myself to holistic therapies, such as acupuncture, aromatherapy massage, colonic hydrotherapy, reflexology, and maybe do a little yoga and have the occasional sauna.

However, it was around this time in my life that I lost my mother very suddenly, quickly followed by my aunt, uncle and cat. It was the most awful eighteen month period. Hypnotherapy helped me come to terms with the anxiety and grief, which most definitely exacerbated my symptoms. I am now delighted to say that not one antibiotic has passed my lips since a bout of cystitis in May 2005, brought on by a holiday in India. I was also taking Malaria tablets, but they made me feel so awful, that I stopped taking them.

I have just read this section back to myself and even I have to admit that I do sound like a hypochondriac! I have gone into so much detail here about my own personal situation because I want fellow sufferers to read it and think "I've got that. That's just exactly how I feel. I'm not mentally unstable after all!" It really is incredible how many of us experience such random and similar symptoms. It is difficult some days yourself not to actually believe that you are not just a malingerer. The classic joke applies here: "The only illness that I haven't got is hypochondria!" My response to this is: "Even hypochondriacs have to die of something!"

Hopefully, now that you are reaching the end of my book you are feeling more optimistic about what lays ahead and may even be looking forward to it. I am living proof that the diet works. I don't want to think about where I would be now if I had not met Katherine all those years ago. All I do know is that I would not be feeling as pain-free and healthy as I do now. Even if I help just one person on their road to recovery, then this will all have been worth it.

Finally, I would love it if you would join my Facebook page: "Candida Can Be Fun!" where everyone can support each other to keep on track.

Raising a champagne glass filled with fizzy mineral water and a slice of lemon to you:

*"Good health!"*

# CHAPTER 7

## SUPPLEMENT ADVICE AND HOLISTIC THERAPY TREATMENTS FOR CANDIDA SUFFERERS

*by Katherine Dempsey ITEC, DIP D-T RGG, AoR*
*Nutritional Consultant and Reflexologist*

Candida
Can Be Fun!

So the diet is hard enough!!! Now it is time for you Candida sufferers to get your supplement programme organised. I suggest that you concentrate on the diet for a month before you start adding in any supplements. The diet you will be on is very nutritious and your body will hopefully start to metabolise the vitamins and minerals in your food on its own.

After you have been starving the Candida in your gut for one month, it is now time to start to kill it off. Before I talk about the treatment, I should mention, at this stage, what will start to happen to your body as the Candida begins to 'die-off':

*Katherine Dempsey*

## 'DIE-OFF' (THE HERXHEIMER REACTION):

As the Candida starts to die, it releases toxins into the bloodstream, which move on to your liver. The feelings associated with 'die-off' are generally an exacerbation of previous symptoms, in addition to some joint pains and 'flu' like symptoms. If you get severe 'die-off', a good way to control it is to adjust the level of antifungals recommended, drink plenty of water and take a large dose of vitamin C to a level where your bowels loosen. This helps to aid the liver in processing the toxins from the Candida.

## ANTIFUNGALS:

So let's get started. To kill off the Candida, I recommend a course of antifungals.

There are many different types; BioCare sells the best range, but you can find one to suit you and your budget:

## CAPRYLIC ACID (Mycopryl):

First discovered in the 1930's, this is a fatty acid found in coconut. The best form is Calcium Magnesium Caprylate, which ensures it can reach your large intestines and kill off the Candida. It comes in three strengths: 250mg, 400mg and 680mg. I use the lowest strength for children and severe cases of Candida. Most clients start with the 400mg, three per day (with food) for the first five days. Upping gradually until eventually they are having two with each meal. If 'die-off' becomes too unpleasant, the level can be decreased at any time and stabilised until the symptoms subside. Once you are taking six 400mg per day and not experiencing 'die-off' you can then take the 680mg dose. Build up gradually, as before, until you are up to six per day. During this time remember to stick to the diet; if you lapse, you will be feeding the Candida again. Caprylic Acid is the best antifungal to use for Candida in the digestive tract.

## OREGANO COMPLEX:

This antifungal plant oil has a short-chain fatty acid structure, making it ideal for treating Candida in outlaying body tissues (muscles, joints, skin, sinuses, etc.). As with Caprylic Acid, it should be increased over time to allow for 'die-off'. The maximum dose is two per day. Remember, Oregano is a herb and can therefore upset a sensitive stomach.

## PAU D'ARCO:

This is a South American tree which has antifungal properties. It usually comes in a blend with other herbs like Barberry Bark and Goldenseal.

## GRAPEFRUIT SEED EXTRACT (Biocidin):

This is a great alternative to the stronger Oregano Complex. This active antifungal oil has been used to reduce bacteria and yeast in the gut, whilst helping to maintain the balance of intestinal flora. The dosage is three capsules taken daily with food. It also comes in droplet form.

This is a vital part of the programme. Once you have put in all the hard work to starve the Candida, then struggled through the 'die-off', you need to replace the 'bad guys' with the 'good guys'. Beneficial Bacteria (Lactobacillus Acidophilus) also known as probiotics, is commonly found in yogurt, but for your purpose you are going to need a high strength capsule containing freeze-dried Lactobacillus Acidophilus, together with Lactobacillus Bifidobacteria. I recommend capsules containing upwards of four million live organisms, four times a day for one month and then decreasing to twice a day thereafter.

## SUGAR CRAVINGS:
One of the main issues surrounding Candida is the problem of sugar cravings. For all this time, your Candida has been making you crave sugar. After all, it is what feeds the yeast, so it is in the Candida's interest to get you to consume as much as you can. When you start the anti-Candida diet, you cut out virtually all sugars and so your system may react. Here is a helpful supplement to take:

## CHROMIUM:
This works to guard against sugar cravings, helping to support glucose and blood lipid metabolism. Chromium is a constituent of Glucose Tolerance Factor (GTF). Found in a liquid form, it is readily absorbable and good for those who struggle swallowing tablets.

*Kinesiology test kit*

## LEAKY GUT SYNDROME:
You may have read about the connections between Candida and Leaky Gut. I am a firm believer that the two generally go hand in hand. Your gut wall is your barrier to good nutrition. A healthy intestinal tract acts as a natural barrier, which prevents large molecules and undigested proteins from entering the circulation. If it is compromised, then particles, especially yeasts, pass through into your bloodstream.

Therefore, anyone with Candida symptoms systemically throughout their body (i.e. recurrent sinus infections, joint pains, urinary tract infections, dizziness), in addition to the very debilitating conditions affecting the mind, should use a supplement to strengthen their gut wall:

## PERMATROL:
This is a fantastic supplement for just that purpose. It contains L-glutamine for intestinal cellular growth and function. N.A.G. (N-Acetyl D-Glucosamine) is an amino acid that occurs naturally in the human body, which helps promote the good bacteria, in addition to strengthening the mucosa (the lining of the gut) which will have been damaged by the Candida. Dosage is three capsules taken daily before food.

## FRUCTOOLIGOSACCHARIDE (FOS):
It may also be helpful to introduce a Fructooligosaccharide (FOS) which supports the growth of beneficial bacteria and forms part of a group of compounds found in raw fruits and vegetables, such as artichokes, chicory and dandelion. It is a natural fibre that encourages the natural peristalis (movement) of the bowel, thereby helping bowel movement and elimination. It does not elevate the blood sugar levels.

## LIVER SUPPORT:
It is vital, throughout your diet and treatment, that you support your liver. It is under intense pressure trying to detoxify all those dying Candida cells, so supporting it is an essential part of the supplement programme:

**MILK THISTLE (Silymarin):**
This is a good herbal liver support which can be taken in supplement or tea form. BioCare also do a Milk Thistle Complex which contains turmeric, artichoke and black radish, all found to help detoxify the liver. It is a good idea to start this supplement as 'die-off' begins. Continue taking it for two to three months.

**IMMUNITY AND GOOD ONGOING NUTRITIONAL SUPPORT:**
Most good health food stores sell good quality vitamins and minerals. If you are mindful of your budget, ensure you spend on the antifungals and probiotics and maybe get a cheaper multi-vitamin. Building up your immunity is vital at this point. You may consider an immune booster like Echinacea or Garlic.

**AWARENESS OF SUPPLEMENTS:**
When buying supplements, I tell my clients it is like buying wine (which, of course, you won't be doing for a while, I'm afraid!). Do not go for the really cheap stuff and, similarly, do not buy the most expensive ones; somewhere in the middle is just right. Some of the very cheap supplements contain 'fillers' like talc, sugar (and its various derivatives) and even yeast!!! So make sure you read the labels first. Maybe you will want to buy your good quality antifungals and probiotics from one main company and your basic multi-vitamins from a more basic range.

**YOUR SUPPLEMENT SHOPPING LIST:**
After you have been on the anti-Candida diet for one month, you may start taking the supplements mentioned below. You may wish to arrange an appointment with your own qualified Nutritionist, so that they can personally assist you through the coming months and help you decide when it is the right time to come off the supplements. In the meantime, I would recommend the following:

**Week 4    Antifungals:**
Caprylic Acid (Mycopryl), Oregano Complex, Grapefruit Seed Extract (Biocidin) (whichever one suits you and your budget). Follow the dosage, but remember to take with food. If 'die-off' is vigorous, cut back the strength or the amount taken.

**Week 5    Acidophilus:**
Get a high strength tablet and ensure it is dairy-free and yeast-free, etc. Take an hour after your antifungal. Permatrol: If 'Leaky Gut Syndrome' is prevalent, protecting your gut wall is most important.

**Week 6    Liver support:**
Consider taking a FOS, basic multi-vitamin and mineral.

**DISCLAIMER**
The information in this chapter has been designed to educate and inform only. The supplements listed should not be used as a substitute for a balanced diet, nor are they meant as a meal replacement.

- Seek proper advice from a Nutritional Consultant when embarking on a long-term supplement programme.
- If you are taking prescription medications, or are under medical supervision, please consult a Doctor before taking any supplements.
- Some supplements should not be taken if pregnancy is planned.

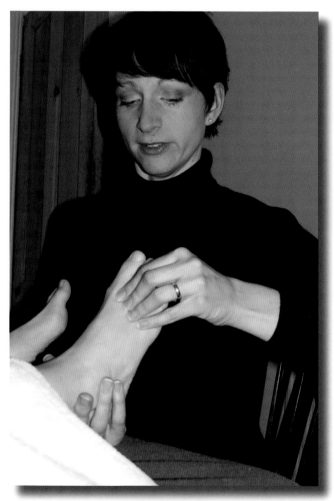

*Reflexology*

## COMPLEMENTARY THERAPIES:

What follows is a brief synopsis of some of the treatments you might like to try to ease your symptoms. If you can, ensure you find a fully qualified therapist with an understanding of treating Candida.

### Reflexology

All foot massage is relaxing and good for stress relief, but reflexology provides a more specific way of working to diagnose and stimulate health within the body. It helps to relieve pain and restore the body's natural well-being. When treating Candida Albicans, reflexology can specifically help cleanse the body of toxins and impurities and hence revitalise energy levels. A course of treatment will help with the symptoms of 'die-off' and help to support the liver.

### Aromatherapy (Massage)

Essential oils have been found to have therapeutic properties for centuries, the oils are often incorporated into massage, or used in baths, or simply evaporated into the air in a burner. The use of pure essential oils with massage helps the body to de-stress and lymphatic drainage aids liver detox.

### Acupuncture

An ancient Chinese system of healing that involves the use of fine needles inserted into the body at specific points to achieve a particular therapeutic effect.

*Aromatherapy massage oils*

Acupuncture's main principle is that of a vital force running through the body (chi), this chi can become unbalanced or out of harmony, and the aim of acupuncture is to find the pattern and underlying causes of this disharmony and rectify it by needling the particular points within the body.

### Shiatsu

Based on the same principle of acupuncture, but using the acupressure points without the use of needles. The application of pressure is the underlying method. Stretching exercises and other corrective techniques are included in the treatment with the intension of creating flexibility and balance in the body, both physically and emotionally.

### Other Self Help

Exercise is vital for your body's well-being, gentle at first, taking advice from a qualified gym instructor. Alternatively, a course of Yoga will help to tone and re-energise the body.

If and when you can afford it, try each treatment at least once and see how you get on with them. You'll be amazed at how much better you will feel for just taking 30 minutes out of your busy schedule to do something for yourself!

*"It's time to de-stress and start feeling good again … mind, body and soul."*